BACK ON TRACK

Learning To Move Forward
in the Face of Change

By

JUDY FRAZIER COMPTON, Ph.D.

Cover illustration by Lonny Matlock.

Please visit the author's website:

www.judycomptonbooks.com

ISBN 1-58597-316-5

Library of Congress Control Number: 2004118092

LEATHERS
PUBLISHING

A division of Squire Publishers, Inc.
4500 College Blvd.
Leawood, KS 66211
1/888/888/7696
www.leatherspublishing.com

Disclaimer

Is this story true? Is it about me? Are the other characters real? The questions are many and varied. My story includes both truth and fiction. Some of the names are real and some are made up. It is fiction based on fact. Most of the story is simply how I viewed life-changing events, and what I did to get *Back On Track*.

— JFC

CONTENTS

To all the "Janes, Joes and Judys" of the world faced with
a major change. This book may be used as a "how to"
manual for people who are thrown into the up-and-down
chaos of corporate America.

When I graduated from high school, the norm was to
marry, have children and maintain a home. Working was
something a woman did to supplement the family needs,
certainly not to put much emphasis on a career of her own.
This role for women was changing drastically as a significant number of women were starting to think in terms of
a career rather than a job. My rural Midwestern roots and
the values associated with them would see many changes.
**The anticipated smooth ride was starting to have a few
bumps.**

My educational quest would be ongoing throughout most
of my life as I did it periodically on an as-need basis. When
I finally had the opportunity to pursue that goal, there
was no stopping. I became obsessed with the idea and ran
the race of my life. **The fast track had begun.**

Once I reached the headquarters of the corporation, I
became aware of career opportunities and wanted to reach
goals that just a short time ago would have seemed impossible. **The uphill climb is difficult at times, but can
be very exciting.**

ACKNOWLEDGMENTS

There were a few friends who read parts of my book as I worked on it. They offered advice and encouragement. Others offered assistance in a number of different ways. I have come to understand that very few things can be done effectively alone. Most of us need some private time to think and rest, but also need the company of others. I am a social being, and friends came alive to me again while writing, even when it had been a long time since I had shared any time with them. I hope my book will be a friend and a help to you, too, as changes occur.

Thanks to Katie, a public relations representative for Bass Pro. She came into my life by chance through a fellow railroader. Her father authored four books and she had been an integral part of those publications. She was and is an inspiration to my writing.

Thanks to my readers. Thanks to Lonny Matlock for using his skills as an artist to design the cover. Thanks to the people who allowed me the opportunity to profile a portion of their lives.

Thanks to all the authors who have shared their words with me. I tried to reference each of them as I quoted material, but often their words stay with me long after their names may have vanished from my memory. So many wonderful writers have enriched my life.

Finally, thanks to all the others. In particular, my family, friends, coworkers, and people who have come and gone during my journey. They have all played a part.

INTRODUCTION

IT WAS LATE October 1989 in Fort Worth, Texas, and supposed to be the fall of the year. I recently accepted a transfer from Springfield, Missouri, and I had just arrived to report for my new position in marketing with a major railroad. Would you believe I had taken all the wrong clothes with me? It was still very hot in Texas. Reservations had been made for me in the Hyatt Hotel for a few weeks until I could find a place to live and get accustomed to the area. The Hyatt was next door to the large corporate office building I would be working in. I had never been this nervous or scared. The Hyatt was beautiful and it is the hotel where John F. Kennedy spent his last night before his death. There were some interesting pictures in the hallway of important guests and entertainers who have stayed there. I should have been very intrigued and excited. The same things that are such a treat on vacation, such as a maid pulling the covers down on the bed and leaving candy on the pillow, were now irritating me. It had suddenly become an invasion of my privacy. My clothes, which were too hot to wear anyway in this warm climate, were in the way, and I was experiencing grave misgivings. What was I thinking?

When morning finally came, I knew that I must dress, control my emotions, look professional, and cross the two-minute walkway to the office where my new job as staff assistant to a marketing vice-president was awaiting. It would prove to be a long walk. Where had the person gone who always had a wanderer's heart and longed to experience new adventures? She had suddenly betrayed me and was nowhere to be found. I completed my walk to the Continental Plaza Building and found the bank of elevators that would take me to the 36th floor. My office area was secluded and had a beautiful view of the city, including a glimpse of railroad tracks. Maybe this was a railroad after all. My new boss was already there and was pleasant to me in a detached and very serious manner. This was comforting, as I was in no mood to participate in conversation at this point. It had occurred to me that I might not be able to communicate with these people at all. What would we have in common?

Soon others were coming into the office. They were friendly and helpful to me. I tried to learn names as quickly as possible, hoping they would like me if I remembered their names. Very little was expected of me that day. The person who previously held my new position came by with instructions and introduced me to a woman who would become a good friend during my stay in Texas. At this point I was enduring, and things were progressing as well as anyone could expect. My eyes kept going to the window, as it seemed impossible for me to be sitting there. Thirty-six floors up was an adventure in itself. The window also allowed me a view of the freeway, which had come alive. I could see what looked like a thousand cars all going every direction as they maneuvered the mix master. I could not even begin to address getting on that highway in my car. At least not that day; it was a matter I would deal with later.

A lesson to learn early in life is that nothing ever stays the same. Within a few days my little alcove had been invaded and people had more in store for me to do. We had approximately 50 people in our department and that many more sales people in the field. The field people were located in various parts of the United States and Canada, but answered to "Headquarters" which was the Fort Worth office. My responsibilities included taking care of all the department needs, such as planning sales meetings, department meetings, sales promotions, and most important of all, customer-related events of all kinds. I did not feel prepared at all. These people did not seem to know nor be concerned about rail service. They were sales-oriented individuals. My senses were still fighting all these new challenges, but the actress I always knew was lurking inside me now had to take command of her finest performance. I was here, ready to accept the challenge of change.

After actually living through the first day of my new position, I now found myself in the second day. Yesterday, I was ready to accept any new challenge thrown my way. Day two was another story. Very soon, the person who would become my mentor, a marketing director, began insisting I go to college and complete my degree. He also advised me that I was signed up for a six-week Dale Carnegie course. How could I refuse? I was wondering how I could even get to work on the freeway, and he was telling me I must venture out at night! And who and what was Dale Carnegie anyway? This person became a wonderful advisor, and I realized he was helping me to grow and make myself credible for future promotions. Oh, but please, not yet!

During the next month I practiced driving on the freeway, moved to an apartment; began the Carnegie course, signed up for two college courses for the spring semester, and wondered: "Who was this woman residing in my body?" Whoever she was, she took the challenge of change literally and was now totally out of control.

The first night of the Carnegie course was something one would choose to forget if possible. Another coworker in our department and I met at the facility, and together he and I went in for what amounted to six weeks of torture. They critiqued our speeches, and if you had any shyness at all, they discovered that perceived weakness and proceeded to rid that from your personality. Speeches started at two minutes graduating upward. Subjects were varied, and in all honesty, a person does get some good experience at speaking. Class size consisted of up to 40 people and the evening seemed to go on forever. By the end of the six-week session I had won some pens and achieved their definition of success. My new coworker, who should have offered friendly support, turned out to be the hardest of all to deal with, as he found joy in returning to work the next day to give a full report of the class activities that had taken place the evening before. In particular, he enjoyed expressing my participation in those activities. I played the part as well as I could if you considered that I was in a group of marketing people who were, for the most part, highly educated, young, competitive and comfortable in the sales arena. That was only the beginning.

The people who worked for the Hyatt became friends and gave me little directional maps to help me find my way around the Dallas/Fort Worth area. They would draw these little maps for me to follow in my car after work as practice runs to familiarize myself with the freeway situation. I am confident that people who have not driven on major highways in large cities have no idea the decisions that await a person who needs to get on and off a major highway in dense traffic. Dallas has five lanes with off ramps on both sides. I had the illusion that all ramps would veer off to the right. That was not the case. The Dallas scene was to come later. At this point, not only had I not left Fort Worth, I had only been a few miles from my hotel and would have been happy to stay right there. Weeks were now passing quickly, and I could feel the anticipation of another change. I was now actively looking for an apartment as close to the office as I could find. That new venture would come soon.

My mentor spoke to me again about college courses. He said I needed to get signed up for the spring semester, and he suggested I go to the junior college located nearby. He insisted I leave early that day and check out what was available. After I reviewed my city map and devised my route, I made my way to the college. I had never paid much attention to maps in the past. However, just as my stay in Texas opened many doors for me, maps became very important. Maps are now close friends of mine and go with me everywhere I go. The college was relatively easy to find and I soon made my decision. It was going to be difficult to tell them at the office what courses I had chosen to take, but hopefully, as sales people they would understand. I was very nervous by the next morning, now realizing they would not be happy with my choices and wondering what I was going to say. It did not take long for the question to be asked, and I had to tell them I was signed up for golf and horseback riding. It was the only time I can recall sales people in my office being speechless.

After they recovered from my lack of understanding on the purpose of college, the teasing began. Whatever some people perceived of me then, this college experience, in particular, turned out to be one of the most positive life changes to ever happen to me. After completing the sport courses, I signed up with Dallas Baptist University to pursue a business degree. The university had a program geared to working adults, and classes were available nights and weekends with a very concentrated program. The university was in Dallas, and this meant driving the freeway during rush hour traffic with not a minute to spare. I learned to leave the office in Fort Worth, endure the food from a drive-through restaurant, eat on the way, and drive 40 miles in five o'clock traffic to achieve this goal. Like so many adults returning to college, I became obsessed with good grades.

It was becoming clear to me that major changes were occurring and my job was becoming a career. Was this the same person who went to school in a rural area and whose major goals were being a cheerleader, editor of the yearbook, and in school plays? Our life's journey may be long or short, perceived as successful or mediocre. But, for most of us, there will be unf stances that require immediate decisions, and we ward into the role of "change agent." My good worker, Phil, introduced those words to me, anc experience I have come to understand what they mean. Throughout the ages, people have had to assume the role of change agent as they encounter life's adjustments.

I want to share with you some of my encounters with change and introduce you to some special people who have also made some major life-altering decisions. I have spent most of my adult life working for a railroad. I am sure that I will fall into the railroad language from time to time. Whatever road you have traveled can probably be inserted with your own professional language, whether the field be medical, financial, retail, service, military, or any number of other professions.

My purpose for this book is simple. I experienced changes and conditions that brought me into a new dimension. I feel compelled to share those thoughts and feelings with others so that they, too, may learn to embrace — and not fear — change.

So, please, do come along for the ride.

1

THE COUNTRY GIRL GOES
TO WORK IN THE CITY

Background

EMPLOYEE SITUATIONS STARTED to change drastically in 1980 following the merger between the railroad I worked for and another even larger railroad. I am sure this was true for employees of other major corporations going through similar mergers. After all, this was the new wave in corporate America.

I was working in the Freight Claim Department and had what was considered a good job. I was in a position to help my family financially, but not required to go beyond the regular eight-hour workday. From the day my daughter was born, I had always made such a big issue of being home with her during her formative years, and I had no intention of changing that habit. But periodically we would be asked to work five hours on Saturday to catch up on our never-ending workload. The chief clerk would ask me to work overtime, and he would then proceed to tell me why I should not. He explained that because I, a female, was working for the rail-road, I was taking a good job away from a man who was providing for his family. He made it clear to me that he would not allow his wife to work outside the home. This was a very hurtful thing to say as women of my generation already felt a strong sense of guilt by working simply due to the culture we lived in. Unfortunately, the chief clerk's wife was in a hospital for the mentally ill, and I could not see how he could bring his personal situation and views into the work environment or make any assumptions about me on such a personal level. But even though our views did not blend as to the "why" of working, I did have this job, and I had to decide about whether I deserved it or not. My need to be home outside of my normal working hours was personal and, therefore, I devised every excuse possible to get out of being required to work overtime. At this point, I had a job, not a career. I say this just to stress how much of a homebody I really was during that period of time. How is anyone ever prepared to know how to make decisions and face the many challenges that confront all of us? Everything was about to change for me and my family as work situations started to have a direct effect on our being able to meet our financial needs. During the next few years, my husband, Jason, and I would face life-changing decisions involving our employment.

Jason worked for a successful truck line in our community. The founder of the company had put his life into the growth and success of the company but was retiring due to health reasons. Terminals were located throughout the Midwest with several thousand employees. The successors of the company were his daughter and son-in-law. In a very short time, it was apparent the company was in trouble. One evening we went to pick up my husband's check and the gates were locked. Not only was that check lost, but also his job and benefits. We were left with an overwhelming sense of betrayal. How could this happen and what would we do? This development in my husband's job would be a strong factor in what I would decide to do concerning my job situation. He was also taking night classes at Drury University, and it would be necessary to stop that expense and address a career change for him.

By 1989 a major portion of the railroad's senior staff and office positions had been moved to St. Paul, Minnesota. We also had offices in Overland Park, Kansas, and a few jobs in a number of other regional locations. But the big rumor going around now was that everything was going to be moved to Fort Worth, Texas, due to some huge tax advantages for corporations versus the tax burden of a corporation that had headquarters within the state of Minnesota. I wondered how a major corporation could simply uproot several hundred families for an alleged tax advantage. Regardless, the railroad headquarters was transferred to Fort Worth and plans were underway to build a huge campus facility at that location. I was the last person most people would consider to leave my home to work out of state, but again, big changes had happened to us. My supervisors were aware of what had happened to the trucking company and knew that my job had become much more important to our family. They discussed possibilities of employment in other areas and offered their assistance. I barely listened. I had no intention of leaving Springfield to work elsewhere. A friend of mine, Pam, casually asked me if I would ride down to Fort Worth with her to look things over as she was considering a transfer there. I found myself agreeing to go with her and I personally wondered why. I assumed it was curiosity or that I wanted to help her make the big decision. Another strange thing happened; it seemed only right that I should see that my resume was updated and prepared to distribute should a future opportunity await me. It seemed as though I was protesting such a move with my voice, but my actions were indicating something far different.

We were on our way! The weather was warm but it rained incessantly. It seemed to be monsoon season in that part of the country, and it was not impressive to us. At one point we were on the wrong highway and we found ourselves in Dallas. Whoops, wrong city. When you have lived in a city of under 200,000 people, the Dallas/Fort Worth complex is another world. Arlington is between Dallas and Fort Worth and it has twice the population of Springfield. I reluctantly got out the maps and started the search to see where we might be and how to get to Fort Worth.

Pam's ten-year-old son was with us, and neither he nor his

mother appeared the least bit nervous about this incident. In fact, they took time to stop the car, get out various snacks and have a picnic. This was unbelievable to me. After their picnic break, we somehow got the vehicle headed back west and ended up in Denton, some 30 miles north of Fort Worth. We encountered great confusion between Highway 35E and Highway 35W as it appeared both were primarily a north-south route. We came to realize that exceptions abound regarding these two highways and many others had experienced the same difficulties and frustration of traveling down the wrong road. We were now heading what seemed to be west on 35, but on the map it appeared north. Now if you can follow all this, it is amazing, because it was months into my Texas life before I realized 35E is Dallas and 35W is Fort Worth. The highways split for both cities and unite again at the north and south ends of the cities. The question of this highway impasse had no attainable answer for us that day.

Pam was ready to head north toward home and forget the whole reason for being there, but I felt compelled to see the office. We finally found Fort Worth and the office building in the downtown area. We felt as though we had just made a great accomplishment. We looked the area over, and Pam decided she was not interested in transferring to Fort Worth. I, on the other hand, felt I should go inside. Pam and her son stayed in the car (I would guess they were having another picnic). I went into the huge office complex with no expectations of meeting anyone I would know. By chance (or was it by some unknown intervention), I met an acquaintance who had previously worked in Springfield, and was now in the human resource department in Fort Worth. He asked me what I was doing way down in that part of the country, and I told him I really did not know, but guessed I was bringing my resume. He immediately introduced me to a few people, and one of them told me I would be hearing from them soon. The building and every-thing around the downtown area was so big, so impressive. With relief, I was certain nothing would ever come from the conversation. How could a small town girl from Clever, Missouri, with no formal education, ever be considered for a position in such awesome surroundings?

I found Pam and her son and we went back home to Springfield. Pam was adamant about the area and stated, "I do not plan to work there even if they move everything to Texas, and furthermore, I do not plan to ever visit there again!" So much for big statements, as Pam did eventually transfer to Fort Worth. She has lived and worked there for the past ten or more years. But at that moment, we were both glad to be on our way home and planned to stay there.

The very next week, a personnel director headquartered in Springfield called me to his office and advised that I would be flying to Fort Worth for an interview the following Tuesday. The job for which I would be interviewed was that of an administrative assistant to a marketing vice-president. Sheer panic started to consume me, but lightened as I realized after being interviewed they would know I was not suitable for a job there. My husband was also beginning to understand that we could be facing some major decisions and/or added trauma in our personal lives. We were again going through a forum of adolescence as we were both too young to retire and too old to look for another job. Surprise! Again, Jason had just lost his job at the trucking company, as did all employees, due to the folding of the company and what appeared to be the greed of the owners. This ended any chance he had for a good retirement with them, which had been in view just over the horizon. Now we must do all possible to save the retirement potential I had with the railroad.

At this point, it is necessary to understand my upbringing, religion, commitment to family, as they all came into play. Our daughter was preparing to graduate from college and get married. She would be okay. The final decision was for Jason and me to prepare for the long-distance life style ahead. We compared the situation to a military family in which separations are expected. My husband would be faced with continuous questions regarding my relocation out of state, and he would be faced with other inquiries from family and friends for the duration of our work situation. It surprised me how long people could ask the same personal questions regarding my stay in Texas. Some of my close friends and family continued to say things to me in what appeared to be an attempt to persuade me to come home. In reality, it only served to make me feel guilty and alone in my career quest. We had made the decision due to a number of reasons, and it would have been nice if they could have wished us well. Some of my extended family members said unkind things to my parents, only serving to increase their concern at my going so far away, alone. But it is important to note that other friends and family gave us continuous support throughout.

My husband, daughter, close friends and family members all made the trip to Texas many times during my stay there. I also learned to make the eight-hour trip by auto, alone, in record time. I was stopped more than once for speeding through the small Oklahoma towns located along Highway 69 between Texas and Missouri. On one occasion, I had left Fort Worth around four in the morning so I could have lunch with my daughter. I guess my foot became a little heavy because suddenly there were flashing lights and a siren. Oh, no, he wanted me! I pulled over and here he came. No smile, only a parental tongue-lashing more severe than I could ever remember from my father. His first words to me were, "How fast do you think you were going through my town?" When I did not respond quickly enough with an answer, he proceeded with question number two and then kept rambling on and on. He never stopped long enough for me to answer. He lectured me for what seemed forever and then gave himself credit for probably saving my life. Maybe he did, because I have never forgotten that lecture and I try to stay as close to the speed limit as I possibly can. He said I was going over 80 per hour. I find that hard to believe (don't you?).

Outside

As women — along with minorities — move up the corporate ladder, they encounter a "glass ceiling." The glass ceiling is an invisible barrier that makes it difficult for women and minorities to move beyond a certain level in the corporate hierarchy. In 1981, for example, only 1 percent of executives in Fortune 500 companies were women, and by 1991 this number had increased to only 3 percent. But the situation is improving, albeit too slowly. Today, the percentage of women who hold the title of executive vice president has jumped to almost 13 percent and is expected to reach 17 percent by 2005.[1]

Coping

The coping skill needed during this period would be identified as dealing with *separation anxiety.* I had been programmed all my life to certain norms and this move was going to stress all of them.

A number of writers have given us some valuable insight as to handling change. I did not write this, but I feel this author of change has a poetic way of explaining:

Life is movement — a powerful ocean churning beneath and about us. We can drift on top, waiting for the calm, waiting for a familiar motion. Or we can take a deep breath and dive in, allowing the wave to push us ahead. We move forward into life, instead of remaining i the drifting state that has been familiar for so many years.

Who are we? Blood, bone, smiles and passion. But insid⟨ the culmination of our experiences. One story linked t⟨

linked to an image, then to another story, each with a message, each adding to our wisdom and self-interpretation. Living is a continuous sequence of moments demanding our participation, not isolation. We cannot change our lives if we cannot transform our moments. The ability to embrace change is like a muscle — learning, flexing, and growing stronger through effort and repetition.

Our lives are habitually colored by our reactions. When we cannot see past these reactions, we miss knowing our true selves. The depth of our ocean remains untapped. Do you want to be "stuck" in old, fixed emotions? Do you ignore this active inner realm? Or learn from it? Many people work on the surface, painting and re-covering and rearranging the furniture. They have never even looked at the structure — the foundation. They don't look because it frightens them.[2]

My formula for enduring during this *separation* was very simplistic. I moved slowly; all the time watching and listening. I was in a new realm with new people. It was important for me to adapt to their ways. And on a more personal level, I watched movies and read books. If there were a weekend in which it was apparent there would be no visitors, then the movie theater nearby would be my friend for the weekend. I hate to admit it, but I have seen as many as six movies at that theater in a two-day weekend. I learned to study the direction, photography, special effects, and any number of other elements that make up a movie. Hobbies work well in these lonely times. My husband played a lot of golf. We do not divulge the cost of phone bills during this time, as they were necessary. My women friends (Sharon, Mary, Jan, Linda, Betty, Karolen and others), phoned, made visits and wrote cards to me. They did not forget.

---

[1] Bateman, Thomas S., and Snell, Scott A., *Management Competing in the New Era,* 5th Edition (McGraw-Hill Irwin, New York, 2002), p. 345.

[2] Oliver, Gene, *Life and the Art of Change* (LifeChange Press, Costa Mesa, CA, 1999), p. viii.

2

ASSIGNMENT, PLEASE: I AM GOING TO FINISH COLLEGE

Education

WHEN DEFINING "EDUCATION," there are many adequate responses. Webster calls it "a process" among other things.[1] I hear people make all kinds of derogatory remarks directed toward the "intellectuals." As a group, they are frequently called "socialists." They are usually guilty of charging students to consider new avenues of thought. Universities and colleges get blamed for many of the negatives within a society. Throughout history, the uneducated have ridiculed "Intelligencia" and those connected with them. Becoming an adult during the turbulence of the sixties made me aware of the impact of students and activism. Who can forget the anti-war protestors on college campuses and the consequences?

My own experience with education is not controversial nor does it carry such consequences. As I assess my educational experiences, I can simply say that I am grateful for having the opportunity to learn from the guidance of others. I did not always agree with them, and it did not always seem necessary to know some of the information, but what a walk! I fought going to college in this new location and invented many excuses, but once involved in the process, I started to understand why this change was necessary for me.

As a child reared in the country, one of my fondest memories is riding my bike to the specified area to meet the bookmobile for my next month's read. The driver/librarian would have a number of books for me and this would be my coming month's adventure. My books would take me to faraway places, and I would meet some of the most exciting characters. Their world became mine and we spent many hours contemplating our next move and solving mysteries.

School was a continuation of these adventures with teachers taking me to increasingly higher levels of the learning ladder. By the time I was in high school, boys and social activities became more important, with books falling well below other interests. By the time high school was over, I was interested in one boy and marriage. We were married, and three years later we were parents of a little girl. This experience is worth an entire book on marriage and parenthood, but not this book.

Beauty School

Education would not be complete without sharing a moment about cosmetology school, commonly referred to as "beauty school." I started when I was sixteen. Looking back, I understand my parents wanted me to have something to do during the summer months besides getting into trouble. I could ride into town with my dad on his way to work. My fellow students were beautiful, worldly women who knew how to look their best. Most of them smoked and looked so cool. Of course, I wanted to be just like them, but it was not to be. I never did learn how to inhale cigarettes and did not like to spend the money on them anyway. The first time I rolled a permanent in a customer's hair, I fainted. The school came to a standstill, with everyone running around in a panic. A similar panic attack happened the first time I saw head lice. I did not faint in that situation, however, and quietly asked the instructor to handle the problem. You can imagine how this experience was going. Cosmetology was not going to be the career for me.

Railroad

Working for the railroad is an education in itself. Each individual position or job responsibility involves some aspect of operating, accounting and communicating. While working in Springfield, we had many opportunities for on-the-job training and I took a few classes at a local university. Just prior to my transferring to Fort Worth, one of my friends and I decided to go to college seriously and get our degrees. We were each walking on a treadmill in the exercise facility at work and discussing how we would go about the venture. Mary was somewhat surprised when I handed her the application the next day so we could get started. However, we did it and started what would be a major change for both of us, albeit not at all what we had planned. As life would have it, we would not go together in our new educational endeavors and help each other for the duration. We would go alone in different states far away from each other. What seemed like such a good plan, when we were making it, was a plan with a number of adjustments. The management of planning must always be done with an eye on change.

A good friend of mine states rather emphatically to me that it is evident from my affair with the bookmobile that I always had the desire to learn. But it was not brought to the surface because I felt inferior. She insists that I wanted to experience formal learning long before anyone else suggested it to me. Perhaps there is a spark within some people just waiting for the right conditions to ignite a burning desire to learn.

Whatever the case, my move from Springfield to Fort Worth put an emphasis on education that appeared to be directed by my work superiors rather than myself. Encouragement to grow in this manner was emphasized to the point that I really saw no way out of it. Obviously, I did not want out of the process because, once involved, there was no stopping. The pursuit of learning became an obsession. Once ignited, the flame became a roaring furnace, virtually consuming every bit of new information that came near.

College

After the golf and horseback riding classes were over, I enrolled at Dallas Baptist University and seriously began to complete my educational endeavors. I became involved in any accelerated method available in pursuit of that goal. I took regular semester classes, summer classes, winter intersession classes, and any other thing I could possibly work into my schedule. My co-workers encouraged and assisted me. My work schedule was flexible enough to allow me to pursue my goal in this fashion. I majored in business administration and minored in business art. My new roller coaster ride was now running at full speed.

During the Dallas Baptist period, my work took a significant new route that instituted more change. I was now working for a new individual with a much disciplined approach to achieving. The general will be described in another chapter of this book, as he deserves more time devoted to him. A concentrated high growth period would begin, not only for me, but for all of us in the office working under his direction. He expected us to give one hundred and ten percent in everything that we did. As he explained it to me from a fighter pilot's standpoint, there was no time for failure or performing second-rate. Perfection was necessary; it could mean life or death. I worked harder than ever to achieve for him, and ultimately, for myself. Failure was not an option.

Students frequently ask me how they can learn to study effectively while also dealing with all the pressures of life. Students just out of high school, with all the decisions and fears, face a unique set of problems. They feel that they must decide at a very young age what they want to prepare themselves to do for the rest of their working lives. Older students usually have family demands, jobs that leave little time for study and school-related issues. The even more mature student, returning to school after a long period since high school, can be even more insecure about college. All age brackets of students face uncertainty and fear. I am quick to let them know that I took classes at each of these stages of life, and each held its own form of anxiety. It is a joke in my family that it took me twenty-plus years to get through school. And now, the difference is that I sit on the other side of the desk, but I am still learning. The important truth in all this is that I do not plan to ever quit the learning process. Learning happens in and out of the classroom.

England

I signed up for various business classes and continued to focus my endeavors throughout the next two years to finish my first degree. Most of my study was in the classroom with the exception of one trip to England. Dallas Baptist had a former professor staying at Oxford University with her husband while he was in the seminary studying to become an Episcopalian priest. She arranged for me to stay in a room in the seminary dorm and experience that lifestyle while using the library and other facilities for an independent study in British rail service.

The Bodleian Library was even larger and more impressive than I had imagined. Visitors are not allowed to touch the books without a card. In order to get a card, I had to furnish three references from Oxford University and swear on a Bible that I would take care of the books. The card only enabled me to check out the books and look at them while in the library. No one is allowed to take the books out — not even the Queen. The library has a copy of every book ever published in the United Kingdom.

The bookstores were full of American books. A clerk told me they had more American publishers than any other, and they were their best sellers. I told her about my school project, and she spent the next two hours helping me look for material. She soon became like an old friend as we shared "talk." The store was expecting a visit from the owner the next day, and they had tried to make everything look perfect. Ah, so very American!

My study also included a report on art history, which was a part of my minor. The elegant beauty of the stately old buildings is forever etched in my memory. Oxford University contains many legends, and many kings and great leaders have graced those halls. I was in awe. The quaint city was also very unique and beautiful.

To understand my awe at this point in my life, it is necessary to realize how far this experience was from my comfort zone. I went to the Dallas Airport, boarded a plane for London, and within a few hours was on five different modes of transportation before arriving in Oxford. I knew I was alone, but I felt assured there had to be a higher "Presence" with me. When I arrived in Oxford, it was turning dark, and all of the buildings looked black, big and foreboding. The taxi took me to the street that I had written down, and now I had to find the correct dormitory. I finally found it, and the professor and the priest, with their two cats, welcomed me in for some long-awaited tea and crumpets. It became apparent my professor friends' expertise was not cooking, but to me — that evening, it was a most sensational meal. Love and warmth permeated the air as we shared stories about their former home in Texas and I learned about their new home in Oxford.

My room in St. Stephens House, a dormitory, had no phone, no television, and only the most basic furniture. I shared the bath with the other dorm residents — all men studying for the priesthood. Since I was the American intruder, and a female, I used that bath only when absolutely necessary. I had taken few clothes, lots of deodorant, a jar of peanut butter, and several boxes of granola bars. These items proved to be the perfect choices.

My American friends took me to the home of an Australian couple for a small party. I found the Australian couple to be most interesting. The Australian gentleman was also studying to be a priest, and his wife was an opera singer. She could not work in the states because she had no green card, but she had been in *Cats* and *Les Mirables* in London. The evening was spent in a manner much like we spend our evenings back in the United States. I was offered an assortment of food and drink and welcomed into their home as a very special guest. They played selections of music from India and America. Later in the evening, the conversation took a much more serious turn when the guests started making light fun of Americans and how one particular incident at the "changing of the guards" made us look very obnoxious and rude. I said nothing, and after the joking about Americans ceased, I realized my feelings were quite on edge. I knew it was not only possible, but it was most likely probable, that we had, in fact, insulted the ceremony. On the other hand, I had just been insulted as a guest in their home. I had been made to feel as though I was the center of a joke they seemed to share. Maybe my hosts, since they were also American, sensed my discomfort. We soon said our goodbyes and left. Early the next day, I received a personal dispatch with a letter of apology for their lack of respect toward me. Evidently, after my departure, they realized how their behavior toward me was exactly what they had been describing about the American tourists toward Europe.

Very soon I met another student from the states who was also doing an independent study. Rose Ann and I would embark on some very serious study of the English. We visited the home of William Shakespeare in the village of Stratford; the theater, his home, Holy Trinity Church, all of which proved to be enchanting. I learned that an Englishman by the name of John Randolph had eight daughters, the youngest of whom married a tenant farmer's son, who was John Shakespeare. By the time Mr. Randolph had all his daughters married, the financial burden of paying dowry costs left him nearly broke. His new son-in-law, John, used the dowry money to become a glove-maker, and he invested in property. He became the town alderman. He took his eldest son, William, to the theater with him on opening nights to see if the plays were suitable for the town viewing. This was the beginning of theater for William.

At eighteen William married a 26-year-old woman of class. On numerous occasions, we sat for hours, listening to enthralling stories of the life and times of William Shakespeare.

In London, we stayed in a rented apartment (E&E Management) within walking distance to the downtown area. This apartment sublet is similar to a timeshare program. The people who own the apartment leave the country and rent to others during their absence. Here I only had to share the bathroom with Rose Ann. Conveniences were few and the furnishings very plain, but it was charming, and I knew I would enjoy staying here.

I had an appointment to meet an official, Mr. Powell, Commercial Director for Research with the British Rail (BR) System, to discuss the differences in European rail systems versus the American rail system. I was going to have to reach him in the north end of London. As you might expect, I had to cross the town.

The British Rail employee gave me specific instructions as to where to board the train and where to get off in order to arrive near his office. The train moved so fast that there was no time to decide where you wanted to get off and on; you just better be ready!

I arrived at Euston Station, exactly as he said I would, and we went across the street to Euston House, which is the British Rail headquarters. The Board of Directors held their meetings here, and a few of the rail offices are in this location. He has had to pay £25 for the use of the meeting room. Even though owned by BR, each division is responsible for all expenses. He had lots of information to share with me in regard to the rail system and why it works so well there. The land area in Great Britain is much smaller in square foot measurement than that of the United States, and the government will subsidize any mass transit needs. The employees are job-protected, and for the most part have lifetime positions.

The paper that I needed to prepare for class required a minimum of thirty pages of information. A group of male executives from the railroad that I worked for had attended meetings in France and Switzerland, and I had access to their notes, so my paper was taking shape. The British Rail employee became my friend, and after my interview with him, we had lunch at an Irish pub across the street with other railroad employees. The day happened to be St. Patrick's Day, and I found it interesting the way drinks and food specials were geared toward that celebration. The newspapers were full of rioting incidents by the Irish in the London area, but my railroad friends seemed unaware.

After lunch, I found my way back to the train station and eventually back to the apartment. Rose Ann's husband had joined us, and we now felt like we could go out at night and see the sights of London in a different light. All three of us loved London! We saw wonderful museums and fantastic plays. Another magnificent learning experience had taken place.

I was able to meet with another American student involved in special courses offered at Imperial College. My family was long-time friends with her parents, and it was obvious they had nothing to worry about. Eva was totally at home in London, could answer questions, and even looked English. We Americans usually stand out very quickly as being different. I was told we convey a self-confidence rarely found in others. Eva had the ability to look both English and American.

My stay also included preparation for a paper and oral presentation on art history. Rose Ann was now traveling with me, and together we were doing the art presentation portion as a team effort. Many of our most famous originals are kept in the museums in London. To see a Seurat original gives a whole new light to what the artist was able to do with dots. Georges Seurat created his greatest work using thousands of dot-like brush strokes. I bought small prints, wrote notes and took pictures, hoping to capture the wonder of art so that my presentation could portray even just a little of the beauty. My art history professor would have us give the presentation on several occasions back in Dallas.

Back in Texas

While involved in the art classes, I also did docent work as part of my class projects. A docent was usually very knowledgeable about certain exhibits in a museum and gave the tour guide information. This was quite enjoyable! My lessons also included assisting with the visiting Catherine the Great exhibit. It is interesting how many avenues of learning are available for the student. Many times a student can be innovative about course credit, discuss the plan with a professor, and independent studies can be arranged. It can be an invaluable asset in the experience of learning.

My degree was nearing completion; I could see the end in sight. By now people were even talking masters programs with me. I was not fighting; I was just not going to do it. My family was miles away and there was talk of job cuts all the time. I simply could not start anything else.

Graduation was here. Of course, I was going. My husband and two other couples came from Springfield for the event. The weekend was a high point of my life. The sense of achievement and endurance is somehow poured into that cap and gown. My group was taking pictures, and we were having a great time. My name was called with the cum laude group, and when the banner was placed around my neck, I felt a sense of deep humility for all who had gone before me in this capacity of learning. That sense of deep humility was to remain with me always. The responsibility of learning and sharing knowledge is overwhelming.

Some of my classes had proven to be very difficult and completely different from prior training I had had. A business degree included a significant number of hours in accounting and finance classes, which require many hours of homework. We formed study groups; and some of the students employed tutors when in real trouble with class work.

The group of people with me sharing this day played a part in my education by their support and acceptance of the time I gave to school rather than to them. On this day, we all shared a special moment. They had all been involved to some extent, waiting for me while I completed a school requirement before we could go out. But on this day, the rest of the evening was spent in celebration and fun. We went to a restaurant near the top of one of the Bass Buildings in downtown Fort Worth and spent a memorable night. The guys could even have a phone brought to them at our table (cell phones were not as reliable yet) so that they could call home and get the SMSU basketball score. It was complete.

Very quickly my thoughts turned to the next educational chapter of my life. Gone forever was the reluctance to further my education. The first degree had proven to me that I could meet the challenge of higher education. This is not to say that I did not suffer with anxiety from time to time and question my state of mind in getting myself into more new undertakings. Change was now becoming a way of life.

After examining the master programs available at various universities in the area, I decided on Texas Christian University. Geographically it was close to me, and everything I saw was very impressive. The program I decided on was called "Perspectives of Society," and it was presented under the masters of liberal arts label (MLA). The classes were geared from a business sociology standpoint. Both the program and the school proved to be very enjoyable. The staff was helpful, and many of them were in the program. I came to know and genuinely care for the people on a personal basis.

Upon completion, I stayed connected to the school through the tutoring/mentoring program. I would spend many hours tutoring a beautiful black woman, who, "answering the call to the ministry," would step into a new world of her own. She was a nurse, a member of the Army Reserves, divorced with one grown son, and was now embarking on the "change of her life." Whenever I thought for one moment that my life was in a constant change process, I looked at her situation. Her weakest area was computer and writing. I was comfortable in those areas. We became a strong team. She wrote her notes and practiced her speeches with me, and I critiqued. As is the case in most educational pursuits, everyone learns something. She related many speeches to me about Calvin and Luther, great religious leaders, and another avenue of learning opened.

TCU holds fond memories and I also attended that graduation ceremony. My good friend, Mary, came for the weekend, and even though we did not celebrate in the same fashion as my first college graduation, it was a lovely afternoon.

By now, the Ph.D. was hovering so very close. I completed most of the course work at TCU and did the dissertation through Columbia Pacific University. I was familiar with authors Barbara De Angelis and John Gray, who earned their Ph.D.s at CPU, so this seemed like the thing to do. All of this work was done independently with highly educated people critiquing and questioning every word that I wrote. This was the most difficult thing I had ever done in regard to education. Attending class provides a teacher, classmates and provocative conversation. Working with a board through computer and telephone puts an amazing amount of pressure on the student. But online courses are being offered today and I strongly support taking them. They teach a certain discipline and time-management in addition to the subject material.

I visited the school facility, but not under a regular classroom scenario. I completed the thesis and it was published. I am proud of it, but there was so much of it that was the idea of others and not really my own. This was yet another level of understanding in how the educational system works. Many times students must adjust their own thinking to the thinking of others, at least for that time period. This experience in learning is one that I cherish as it enabled me to open new doors of opportunity. In my opinion, it is good to experience education by any means available to you. Most of my study was done traditionally at private, expensive universities, and fortunately my employer reimbursed me the cost of the tuition. I realize not everyone is provided such an opportunity. However, if the financial aspect had been different, I hope I would have pursued using grants, loans, scholarships or any means available for the opportunity to learn.

Once a person seeks educational pursuits, they do not always know when to stop going to school and start putting what has been learned to use. The railroad was downsizing, rightsizing, and firing people at this point, and I, too, was let go. Most of us were now past forty years of age, and it seemed some of the senior management saw no need for us. They hired Drake, Beam & Morin to assist us in finding ourselves again after this trauma. Most of the employees at Drake had been through a similar experience themselves and were very empathetic toward us. Because of the need for me to secure my full retirement benefits, it was determined that I should go back to a union job where I still held seniority and could stay with the railroad until an opportunity for early retirement would present itself. This move would put me back in Springfield with my family and friends. And I could see where my educational experience would take me. Up to this time, educational pursuits had apparently failed me.

Teaching

I taught a business class for Ozark Technical Community College at the Federal Medical Center for Prisoners in Springfield in the evening while working for the railroad during the daytime hours. This could have been my first and last experience at this sort of thing. I was told to come to the prison facility at six-thirty in the morning, go to the lighted gate, park in the visitor's area, and come to the main office area. This sounds very straightforward and simple. It was not to be that easy. The sky was dark and rather foreboding that first time. Driving into the prison complex made chills run up and down my spine. Upon arriving, I drove past the gate because I saw no light. I could find no visitor sign and parked in the wrong area. When I got out of my car, two armed officers who had been escorting me since I entered the premises greeted me. A voice from a loudspeaker blared out to them, and the rest of Springfield, that I was okay and for me to continue up the steps and into the building. What a beginning!

As it turned out, the light had just burned out at the gate, the visitors parking sign was being painted, and therefore not marked, and I was just there appearing as an intruder during non-visiting hours. It was evident the armed officers were very amused but could not let it show. I, on the other hand, was not amused, just anxious. After I filled out the required papers and let them fingerprint me, I was permitted to see the educational area. If you have never been inside a prison facility, then I can assure you it is quite an experience. A guard escorted me through several doors, each one slammed and locked behind us. We went deep into the prison complex before coming to the educational area. There were male prisoners in the halls everywhere and very few personnel.

This first teaching experience was a real breakthrough in change for me. I was to be with twenty students, all paying for this class, and they seemed to be taking it very seriously. They were going to be released to go out into the world seeking a job with a felony on their record. I tried to learn all I could about the system and how they could get past such a huge mistake. Most of them were young and were in this facility due to drug-related incidents. One fellow was in for manslaughter. I had been told he and some other family members got in a fight over drug sales, and my student had killed his cousin. He is the one student that I had the most misgivings about, as he appeared to rebel at so many of our culture norms. The fact that he was American Indian and was reared on a reservation in South Dakota may contribute to his unhappiness at much of society.

Another prisoner was in for murder. He arrived in this country from Scotland, and within just a few days after arrival he was accused of murdering an elderly couple in Las Vegas. He insisted he was suffering from amnesia and could recall nothing about that particular time period in his life. The interesting part about this case was that his I.Q. tested the highest on record at the facility. They warned me he could play with my mind and to be aware. He was consumed with getting extradited back to his home country. That part of his memory was intact. He was brilliant in the classroom and a wonderful assist to me. All the others had various levels of drug addiction and selling/distributing illegal substances on their record. It was evident some still talked of drugs with reverence, but most appeared to look forward to a new chance at life, clean and responsible. They were attempting to make their own individual changes as I was making another change in my life.

We bonded to some degree and looked forward to class sessions. I learned a lot about the exchange of learning, and even though I could lead, the students were quick to discuss and assist. I felt I had some information to offer and share in the academic structure.

I also did substitute teaching for the Springfield School System while off work during one of my railroad changes. If you have never been in this environment, then it will be difficult to take you there. On my application, I had stated clearly that I would not be available for music, foreign language or the highest level of math classes. Well, you can imagine what I was called for the first time, yes, music. I insisted that I was not trained in this field. However, they were desperate and in need of a warm body to take control of the class. I arrived for the junior-high level orchestra class and proceeded to conduct an orchestra. Once you agree to something, it can come back to haunt you. I was now down on the list to teach music. Tuning a violin can be a real challenge if you have never even touched one. But, as luck would have it, my many years of piano lessons paid off. I could read music, so we found a middle ground, and together we completed our practice sessions. As this learning process continued, most of my work at substitute teaching was in the area of business classes at Central High School, a very positive experience. Now, I can gratefully give credit to the teachers of our young people throughout history. I found that the little people who wanted you to talk to them and baby them would be excellent future mothers if their nurturing abilities were developed. I found that the bullies, who wanted so badly to show their power, were practicing their leadership skills if channeled properly. I could see my little tattlers as future news reporters and advised them to pursue that route.

Shortly thereafter, I was again sent back to Fort Worth, and believe it or not, a short time later, after yet another downsizing at the railroad, I would find myself back in Springfield teaching again. This time I taught classes for Drury University. Again, the class was off their main campus, to be held at Cox College of Nursing. The Cox System is a full medical facility with a nursing college. Drury furnishes the general education teachers, and I was to teach business and humanities at the Cox location.

My first semester there was intimidating, as a large number of the students were nearing graduation and were advanced in their field of nursing. I knew some of them thought business classes were a waste of their time, but I brought in speakers from insurance, volunteer agencies and other health-related companies. I tried to whet their appetites and broaden their minds to some of the health-related businesses they would be dealing with. As I have moved further into this area, I find many companies are intermingled and all of the students will be stronger knowing the fundamental workings of the business world. As we find ourselves engaged in change patterns, knowledge of different situations can serve to give confidence and guidance.

I have changed the strategy of the class several times now as the United States is seeing a large number of companies being charged with various crimes. The textbook covers various management principles, and I have encouraged the students to understand the combined importance of current events in business and politics and how those events affect their lives on a personal basis. As we address insurance, pensions, 401-Ks, investments and drug companies, it is apparent that the strings of attachment are intertwined throughout. As future managers and employees in the nursing field, they must be abreast of how companies operate.

How can anyone sum up, so to speak, how education played such a role of change in my life? The jobs I have held, places I lived, and the amazing people who have crossed my path have all brought about "Change." Sometimes I fought the changes, other times I relished in them, but always there was something to gain. I can only look forward to what may happen next.

Outside

In this decade the emphasis on education will continue. The industrialization of the United States plants will increase the use of robots, which means that more highly skilled, but fewer workers will be employed in such facilities. Jobs for those with lower skills will be reduced. The use of computers will continue to increase, making it possible for companies to hire fewer people to perform more work. Computer literacy is a must in today's work world. This is the decade of the knowledgeable worker in America, and yet corporations once respected in this country continue to send their work elsewhere to countries outside the borders of the United States.[2]

More

As the population of the United States became increasingly well educated, women made significant gains (Bianchi & Spain, 1986:137). In terms of enrollment, women represent more than 52 percent of the college population. In 1985, slightly more women (50.7 percent) than men earned bachelor's degrees, and about the same number of women as men received M.A. degrees. But women represented only 34 percent of Ph.D. recipients. Differences still exist between men and women in their major field of study. More than two-thirds of students in majors such as architecture, engineering, physical sciences and religion are men. Those fields in which over two-thirds are female include education, foreign languages, library sciences and health professions. But women made significant inroads in traditional "male" areas of study. For example, women recipients of medical and law degrees more than doubled since the 1970s, and women increased substantially in fields such as mathematics and engineering.[3]

Coping

The coping skill needed during this period of my life revolved around *personal growth*. Mentors miraculously appeared at key moments to encourage me and push me beyond what I, and probably others, perceived to be my limits. I, in turn, pushed my daughter to complete college, and she used to tell her friends, "If I don't finish college 'she' will kill me." I don't remember using such a harsh term with such finality, but I did push. People also pushed me, and now I am glad they did.

Learning is finding out what you already know. Doing is demonstrating that you know it. Teaching is reminding others that they know just as well as you. You are all learners, doers, teachers. [4]

Our success or failure depends on what we're taught, what we learn, and what we do with it.

Martin Buber states:

"Everyone has in him something precious that is in no one else."

Louis L'Amour:

"The best of all things is to learn. Money can be lost or stolen, health and strength may fail, but what you have committed to your mind is yours forever."

---

[1] *Webster's Ninth New Collegiate Dictionary* (Merriam-Webster, Springfield, MA, 1990), p. 396.

[2] Connor, J. Robert, *Cracking The Over-50 Job Market* (Plume, New York, 1992), p. 17.

[3] Vago, Steven, *Social Change, Second Edition* (Prentice-Hall, NJ, 1989), p. 181.

[4] Bach, Richard, *Illusions: The Adventures of a Reluctant Messiah* (Delacorte, New York, 1977), p. 46.

3

MORE CHALLENGE:
I CAN HANDLE THIS PROOTION

Career

WHEN DOES A person realize that a job is becoming a career? In my opinion, a career can be as a homemaker, a garment alteration person, or CEO of a Fortune 500 company. The discovery of what you want to make of your work situation can be an important change option. Many people do well at their jobs and want nothing more than to work eight hours, leave their place of employment, and then start what they consider their real life. Others begin their "real" life when they go to work. The best part of their day is going to work and pouring their hearts and mind into their jobs. Most of the time the kind of jobs we have generates the type of fulfillment we can get from them. Too often people take what they can get because they must have an income and the job may have nothing to do with whom they are and what they like to do. Opportunities come and go for many, and some people get few opportunities and must seize any chance to find a job they enjoy. I have found a person must be a risk-taker at times and be willing to accept the consequences of whatever may come from daring to take the risk.

My husband and I were young, had a little girl, and we needed to "get on our feet." I made the decision to get a job. My husband had not made the same decision for me, but he did not stand in my way. I tried to create a resume, but there was nothing to put on it. I graduated from high school and beauty school and had very little work experience. It was obvious I would just have to fill out an application, and all I could think about was that there would be nothing on it but my name. How could I ever get a job if I had no references? At this period in my life, the words "change agent" would have been as foreign to me as the Spanish language. I worried about this for a number of days and then got tired of worrying and decided it was time to go try. I presumed that rejection would be the worst thing that could happen. No one likes rejection and that old enemy can do lots of damage to our self-esteem.

I filled out applications at the St. Louis-San Francisco Railroad, Missouri State Highway Patrol Office, and Lilly Tulip Cup. As luck would have it, while at Lilly, a friend from the neighborhood where I grew up came into the room and visited with me. This visit secured me a job in the accounting department. My first example of how being connected can make such a difference. My application was so bare, but by this person having known me, he was able to give me a personal recommendation. I was starting to realize that having acquaintances and friends along the way could make a dynamic difference. The business world of today refers to this situation as networking.

I worked at the Lilly Tulip job for four months and the highway patrol office called with an opening. Call it shallow, selfish, smart or any number of words, but I took the new job because it offered three weeks vacation and I had a three-year-old. It was agonizing. I felt such guilt toward the wonderful people at Lilly who had given me a chance and such trepidation at leaving a job I really liked to go unto the unknown. My youthful thinking also opened grave misgivings to leaving this job because they had a wonderful cafeteria and you could take free paper products home every Friday. I changed jobs for one reason, and that was time with my little girl.

The new job was not for me. I typed all day, and my typing skills were questionable at that period in my life. I realized I had just made a huge mistake. The words "change agent" were still not in my vocabulary, but changes were coming at me so fast and I was fighting every step of the way. I was starting to build a resume, but it looked like I could not hold a job. What to do now? The railroad had sent me a letter stating they had no openings at this time, but they would keep my application on file for a year. It was considered very difficult to be selected for a job with the railroad. Many coveted these jobs, and a person had to be very persistent to get hired. But I had been hired at two other companies, and I just knew that this was a job I had to pursue. There was a signature on that letter, and I felt it was time to make contact. I did not belong where I was. There is no need for detail. I left my job with the patrol in less than four months. Again, I felt terrible to leave after such a short time, but I was moving on. My long and tumultuous railroad career was beginning, and what a ride it would be.

It was Monday morning and I had arrived at my new job with two amazing pieces of information. First, I was in training and would not be paid. It was assumed that I knew this. All I could think about was that I was paying a babysitter and just how long would my training last? The second instruction was that I would have to join the union and pay union dues. I said nothing as I did not want to appear as if I did not know about such things, but I only wished someone would have told me about the union. Looking back, I realize how the railroad managers would assume I knew those things if I was applying for a job there. On the contrary, I did not recall ever studying about the industrial revolution and how organizations in transportation were set up. It was to be expected that the old sidekick called fear would be coming all over me again. It was like a heat consuming my entire being. It would take many years for me to understand energy and how strong emotions trigger energy forces within us. At that moment, I could only wonder if I had made another big mistake. There were lots of people and they all appeared so professional and poised. The women were well dressed and very attractive. In fact, I had never seen so many pretty women in one place. Fear was now being accompanied with feeling unsure of me as a person. These people were going to be able to see through all my insecurities immediately. The question kept beeping in my brain, "Is my third job going to be over in just a few months now, too?" I now found myself calling on a higher Being, as I did not believe at that moment that I could get through the next hour.

A beautiful woman asked me to eat lunch with her group, and my prayer was answered. As the weeks progressed, I found my niche of friends and realized I could do the work assigned me. Training lasted only a few days, and my job as an accounting type position turned out to be quite easy for me. I found my home away from home. All too soon I heard talk of merging with another railroad which would mean transfers and job abolishments. This kind of information would continue during my entire career, sometimes true, but many times just gossip. Fear would be the primary motivator of these rumors. I held many types of jobs and grew in knowledge and confidence in regard to the railroad. For many, the railroad becomes a substitute or a continuation of family. Most of us became glued to the railroad even though it holds a love/hate element for most of us.

The railroad I worked for, the St. Louis-San Francisco Railroad, better known as "Frisco Railroad," finally did merge with a large railroad. After almost twenty years of rumor, it had happened. All our fears were now going to come full force as we were seeing our work moved to St. Paul, Minnesota and Overland Park, Kansas. The railroad has a long and interesting history with J.H. Hill as the founder. He was a controversial character, but one the railroad had long held in awe. Some of the people were planning their move to St. Paul so that they would have a job. I was planning to go nowhere. I planned to work only a short time anyway and I would quit before I would move. I did inquire from a fellow employee in St. Paul as to how long the summer season lasted. His answer to me, "I believe it was on a Wednesday last year." Can you imagine what that answer would do to a sun-worshiping, tan as I could get, summer lover? The move was not even to be considered. I would stay on here, doing whatever I could, until there was nothing left. And then I would pursue an entirely new career.

A major incident took place that would require me to think "out of the box" in a way I had never had to do before. My husband worked for a trucking company in town. The company was considered successful, and he would be expected to have a lifetime job. Another unforeseen occurrence took place and the business was closed. Through no fault of his own, my husband now had no job. All the emotions connected with job loss were taking their toll on him. The emotions of fear and anxiety would try to invade both of us once again. I did not want to add more stress to him as he faced this situation; he had enough worry at that time. But what would this mean in regard to my job situation? There was great disappointment for me now in more ways than I had expected. I was having thoughts about going to college, getting my degree, and changing everything about my work- related life. I was very interested in the field of nutrition and was secretly dreaming about a new career. Change agent was in my mind, but I had no way to act on it and, of course, I still did not know the phrase at all. Questions kept mounting as to what we should do.

During this period of time, I was working as a network supervisor in the communication department, which included the dispatchers, telephone, radio and computer equipment. We had a great deal of responsibility and excellent mentoring. We were required to pass a test to become a network supervisor, and this required a learned knowledge of ohms law as it pertains to electronics and all sorts of other communication language. But from the department head down, you were taught well and encouraged to learn all you could. It was this environment that probably gave me the confidence and training to feel I could pursue the huge step awaiting me.

I was quite comfortable with electronic equipment and enjoyed my work in this capacity. I had experienced being chief telephone operator and had the opportunity to go with that position when it was moved to St. Paul. But, of course, I could not go to St. Paul. It was too cold and too far away. The dispatchers were moving to Fort Worth and I could get into that area of work, but hesitations were there, too. The call from Fort Worth came just a few days after my visit there. The personnel director in Springfield told my boss, and the two of them told me, that I would be flying to Fort Worth for an interview within a couple of days. This gave me so little time to worry that I just did it. As you might guess, the plane arrived late at the Dallas- Fort Worth airport. Now, through no fault of my own, as the Fort Worth human resource department had made the arrangements, I was going to be late for the interview. I took the first taxi available and found that the driver could speak very little English. I was so naïve then that I could not believe someone I considered a foreigner would be driving in this huge complex of cities and not be able to read the instructional road signs printed in English. Not to mention the ability to speak English. Well, we finally understood each other well enough for him to get me downtown. I was late and the person with the job opening had another appointment within the hour. The interview was fast, and I was grateful that it all worked out like it did. The shorter the interview, the quicker I could get back to the airport and home. Again, my plans were not to be. Three people from the human resource department took me to lunch and I was questioned extensively. One of the women even told me I could stay with her until I found a place to live as she had an extra room. I could not find the words to tell her that I would not be coming to

Fort Worth regardless of how the interview came out. As I recall, I was so deep into the unknown by that time that fear and anxiety were still napping. This was probably an example of how our bodies function by habit when so many new things are happening. I got back to the airport just in time for my flight. I knew nothing about the job decision, and that was just fine.

The call came that I was to report to work in Fort Worth the following Monday. It was arranged for me to stay at the hotel next door for as long as needed to make living arrangements. I took the barest necessities because I did not expect to stay.

Within a few weeks, I would have an apartment and my husband would bring only the basic living essentials to me. This was all very difficult for him as well. He was torn between wishing me well and sounding like he wanted me to go, and acting like he did not want me to go indicating he did not support my decision to try this new job. He was in a Catch 22 with a thousand confused thoughts going through his head. I am sure that drive to bring me my things was one of the longest and loneliest of his life. There was no way we could have envisioned what this type of arrangement would do to us as individuals and to our marriage.

My new position of staff assistant had a variety of duties and proved to be interesting. My boss, a vice president for the marketing department, was distant, but very nice. The executive vice president of marketing, to whom my boss directly reported, was on our floor, and through the coming months I would get to know him as well. They were both experienced in transportation, and I learned quickly the management style that was currently in place. The chief executive officer (CEO) was also someone I would come to know and respect. His offices and boardrooms took up the entire 38th floor. I saw the area a few times and it was most impressive. He had come from the airline industry, and there were models, artwork, and an assortment of transportation-type memorabilia. It was said that he was the only person of Jewish faith, and a registered Democrat who served as a CEO of a Fortune 500 company at that time. He was adept at remembering our names and was a very impressive gentleman.

The director, who became my mentor, told me that good things were going to be happening to me. The job, the people, and above all, the city were affirmative reinforcements of the decision we had made. My family and friends were coming often, and we were all enjoying new discoveries. As changes were happening to me, they were also happening to the people associated with me. My husband was now working for a successful company with potential for promotion. There was no more talk about him coming to Fort Worth any time soon. At this point, I was involved with school and my job. I could not come home now.

It is important to relate my experience at finding an apartment in a huge city. There are so many things to consider. I would drive around and try to see what the people looked like who lived there. I do not know what I was looking for really as the people in a city of this size are so diverse, and the apartments seemed to have every type of person you can imagine. Springfield is a small city with a very low diversity in regard to nationalities. I was not used to this much variety, but I would come to relish in what I discovered about my friends whose outside looks were very different from mine. My apartment choice was in a complex with easy access to the freeway and only minutes from downtown. It was in the city of Arlington, twice the size of Springfield, but very close to Fort Worth where my office was located. Another learning experience was going to occur, as I had never handled this type of transaction before. There are rentals, leases, time constraints, and documents to sign, and on and on. I was in a panic as signing an apartment lease for a year was unheard of to me. I needed to feel I could go home at any moment, and this lease thing was putting lots of new pressures on me. After checking a number of rentals, I found I would have to sign a lease anywhere I went. I signed the thing, we moved my few things in and wondered again what was happening. I had a card table and chairs, bed, dresser, television, computer, a few books and a couch. By the time I left the area for the last time, I had furnished three apartments on very little money, gotten almost all of the money invested back when I sold the furnishings, and realized a person can have a lot of fun making changes. My women friends from Springfield and daughter, Alexis, from Kansas City would visit and we would go shopping to find bargains and make my apartments come alive.

On one occasion a friend came to visit me, flying down with my cousin in a small plane, which was to land in North Dallas. I was to meet them and bring her back to my apartment to spend the night with me. I had only been in the area a few weeks. The panic questions began, how was I to master this dilemma. They all thought I could do more than I thought I could. My maps were out on the table, and I was trying hard to read them. The radio was playing low, when suddenly an announcement seemed to burst forth. The Rolling Stones were going to perform at the convention center downtown, and they were announcing a major traffic problem. I looked back at my map. The highway I needed to take went directly in front of the center. That would mean traffic jams beyond my comprehension. A Higher Power intercepted on this one. My cousin heard the same announcement and knew enough about Dallas to know this would not work. He changed their plans, brought my friend to me, and we all had a very late dinner. He made it a point to visit me on many occasions, always a strong brotherly support.

Now back to the railroad career changes. After working the staff assistant position for a number of months, I started looking at the job postings. Job opportunities were opening up, and I wanted a more challenging position. There was talk that a four-star general was coming on board as executive vice-president of operations. My boss told me I was being considered to work for him due to the fact that I had been with the railroad a long time in a number of capacities and could assist him with basic railroad information. This would be a high profile position and one that I was excited about, but there were many fears associated with working for a man in such a high position with no railroad background. I got the job, and the most intense high-growth period in my life would begin. My belief is very strong that nothing happens by chance; all things are meant to be. At this point in my career, I was becoming a risk-taker and held strong to the belief that when there are questionable decisions, to never look back. The general was now coming on board and I was to accompany him. He had two aides, Phil and me. He was accustomed to six personal aides, a secretarial pool, and any number of others at his disposal. He had not driven a car in six years because of security constraints. It seemed he knew everyone that I read about in the newspapers. In his office, he had a picture of himself with President Bush (P.). He had subtle power that was apparent before I ever met him. For example, on the day I interviewed with him, I wore a suit that was dark blue with gold buttons. It looked just like a military uniform and I had not even realized it until later.

He was head of the Strategic Air Command, stationed in Omaha, Nebraska, just prior to his military retirement. I came to know he was educated in a military academy and the Air Force had been his career. He was a fighter pilot who served in Viet Nam. He had been everywhere and seemed to have done everything. His appearance was very serious, tall, full head of white hair, and he spoke to us in a direct, to-the-point, official manner.

The general became General Jack to the railroad (troops) and Jack to us who worked directly for him. He was still very connected to the military, on the board of four major companies, became involved in the city, and was consumed with changing the safety conditions of the railroad. Several more people were added to his personal staff, as the workload was unbelievable. He expected the people who worked directly for him to perform at "perfect," and if you did not, he would have either you or the work placed elsewhere. Phil and I stayed the course and learned to act and react before anything happened. He instilled in me the absolute necessity of continuing educational pursuits. There was no second best; a person was expected to perform his duties at the very highest level possible. As he patiently explained to us, it could save your life if you were in a life/death situation.

On one occasion when work demands were very high I had a serious health incident. There was an important and expected to be very difficult accounting test that evening and I was totally pushed to the limit. I broke out in such a severe case of hives that only a controversial, experimental drug could take care of the condition. I had never had hives before. Jack told me he had only had hives on one occasion and that was as a fighter pilot dropping bombs on Hanoi and having to fly so low over enemy territory that he could almost feel the heat of the ground. With this equation in mind, I was instructed to take a week off and get well.

During this period, I was so sick that I started thinking they would send me to the Hawaiian Island that was once used for leprosy patients. The rash and swelling seemed to want to stay, but finally I was free. I tried to see a positive side to this incident and made myself envision that it would be nice to have had the time to write my book and drink pina coladas all day while on that island. I did not get well in a week, but I did get well. After this incident, I did slow down a bit, but not much. I did learn how important it is to schedule properly to allow the body and mind to have some rest periods, to rebuild and get ready for the next incursion.

Jack taught me many of the steps in adhering to change. He often took us to a Vietnamese restaurant for a "work" lunch. The most difficult aspect of the work was his requirement for us to eat with chopsticks. He also included me in a work lunch at the Petroleum Club in what was the men's-only area of the restaurant. The law had required the Club to include women on an equal basis, but I was the only female in the room. Risk-taker, change agent, all appropriate to describe one of the many positive aspects of Jack. He was an excellent example to those of us who worked for him.

A number of acquaintances passed through my life during this period of high change who are necessary to mention. I believe it is important to allow people to share your passages along the way. They may be in your life for only a short time or an entire lifetime, but they are often instrumental in the development of who you are. Privacy is almost sacred to me, and I can become quite undone if anyone asks me too many personal questions, but there are times when we must let other people in. There was Sue. I would describe her as a very attractive career woman. She would not describe herself as a feminist, but she proved many of the goals of that group. She was totally self-sufficient. It was much later in our friendship that I found she dealt daily with overcoming a heart condition that killed her father at the age of 38. She picked up children at an orphanage on weekends and provided a very special service to them. She later adopted a high-risk child and cared for her as her own. She had male friends, but never seemed to want to take the marriage plunge. She had overcome so many obstacles that going it alone worked best for her. The day that I moved into the apartment, she brought flowers. When I broke my foot, she took me to the doctor. During the hives episode, she brought food. We do not see each other now, but I will never forget how she filled a lonely gap in my life. If I had shut this door due to my privacy obsession, I would have missed knowing an amazing woman. She is an example of independence and endurance in an ever-changing world. There were a number of examples of spirited change agents that I met along the way. My school friends pursuing the same goals were excellent sources of support. Even though they may have been friends for "only a moment," what a special moment it was.

During this period in my career, I was exposed to the organization of a large company and how information is transmitted throughout the organization. We had vertical as well as horizontal setups, a number of team-based groups, centralized and decentralized. The transportation industry is the perfect atmosphere in which to try everything. The railroad has customers based throughout the United States, Canada and Mexico. Even if I were starting the company at this moment, it would be difficult to determine the best place for headquarters. Even with technology the way it is today with teleconferencing, video presentations, and all other means of technical communication, it is still necessary to meet with your employees and with your customers. Big customers, such as those who mine coal out of the Powder River Basin in Wyoming, are important, but we would not want headquarters there. It is necessary to have adequate air service and be able to reach most destinations in a matter of hours. I had always hoped for our headquarters to be located in Kansas City. My arguments would have been the geographical location within the states, median tax base, availability of housing and goods, and selfishly, it was near my home. Overland Park, Kansas, was considered, but did not make it. The Dallas-Fort Worth area has the large airport facilities, right-to-work state, no state tax, and access to many other large companies. During my stay there, Motorola and several other companies also made their headquarters there. There is also a large contingency of related businesses to be involved with.

I was exposed to the board of director functions and how they relate to the company. They were responsible for selecting senior management, and senior management seemed to select them. The shareholders had an opportunity to vote on them and to at least feel somewhat involved as a stakeholder. There were usually quarterly meetings which, on occasion, were held in our building. After our offices were completed on the campus facility, we occasionally saw the Board of Directors arriving for meetings in the limousines. They were usually successful business people well known in their field. One memorable member for me was Barbara Jordan, a Texas congresswoman, professor, and African-American with a disability who had broken the stereotype many expected and appeared to be the epitome of success. I heard her speak on several occasions, and she was very powerful.

While working in the finance department, we prepared all the information for analyst meetings in New York, and for the board meetings. It was so very important to see that every number and figure was in place for their perusal.

After senior management came vice-presidents, general managers, directors, and a number of other titles. These titles are very important, as they are the determining factor in the grade level that determines salary, bonus and stock options. Ambitious individuals spend many hours devising how best to plan their climb up the ladder.

Another railroad merger was looming and more changes to personnel. The buzzwords were back: downsizing, rightsizing, restructuring and job-cuts. The senior management team and a small group of high profile management were given the golden parachute and were already gone. My mentors and most of the people I knew best were leaving the company. I was placed in budgets, an area of the finance department, and I was downsized from that position. I returned home, in a very short time, I was sent back to Fort Worth to work in equipment, an area of marketing.

This time I did not work in the big office building downtown. We had moved out north of the city into what was called the "campus" concept. There were a number of buildings, and a number of services would be available when the project was complete. There would eventually be a credit union, daycare, restaurant, fitness facility, and a walk/run track on the campus. The most memorable to me was the entrance which was a railroad museum filled with interesting memorabilia and wonderful artwork. Gracing the halls of the buildings was an extensive art collection that was unbelievable. Paintings would come and go as they were loaned out to other museums. There were four railroad business cars located at the entrance, refurbished as they had been in their most elegant era. We entertained customers in them.

The control center was first-rate as well; even the secretary of transportation made a visit to see this futuristic area where the train dispatchers and rail operations personnel did their jobs. It was a huge circular area with giant screens and viewing rooms at different levels. It was almost like a small stadium, in that you could watch from so many locations.

Through the years I worked in and out of many departments, accepting change and challenge along the way. There were many positives and a few negatives, but it was all for a solid learning experience. As someone once said, "How would we recognize the hills if we never experienced the valleys?"

It is not a myth that the workplace still contains prejudice, unfair practices, and the buddy system. I saw people promoted to positions well out of their reach of expertise who went to the same church as the boss, or who had drinks after work with the boss. I worked with people who would wash the car for the boss on Saturday to make points with him. I also saw jealousy and envy directed toward people, causing them to lose the chance for a promotion they were well suited for. It is gut-wrenching for people to want a position so badly, and be so right for it, and see it handed to someone who appears not to have worked for it at all. But it happens, and to survive in the workplace a person must accept to some degree and move on. Large companies put in programs geared to eliminate or at least lessen this type of practice, but it is very difficult to eradicate completely. The human resource departments may have an entire staff directed toward diversity, but statistics still indicate there is much to do. The workforce statistics are indicative of major changes in numbers of certain groups, so it will be interesting to watch how this plays out in promotions of the future.

My career climb was cut short. I fought it in the most powerful way that I could. I filed an age-discrimination suit against one of the most powerful companies in the United States. I was prepared to accept that they could not let me win and would do whatever it took, because they could not let such a case win. Too many older people had been let go, and it would stir up too much bad publicity. But I also knew that for anything to ever change, a stand must be made. I made the stand and it turned out as expected. Would I do it again? Maybe, but if I did, it would be done different. I learned so much.

Outside

The macro view was starting to appear ominous for American workers during the eighties. To quote from one business writer with an eye on the future for workers:

We are living in the time of the parenthesis, the time between eras. It is as though we have bracketed off the present from both the past and the future, for we are neither here nor there. We have not quite left behind the either/or America of the past—centralized, industrialized, and economically self-contained. With one foot in the old world where we lived mostly in the Northeast, relied on institutional help, built hierarchies, and elected representatives, we approached problems with an eye toward the high-tech, short-term solutions.

But we have not embraced the future either. We have done the human thing: We are clinging to the known past in fear of the unknown future. Those who are willing to handle the ambiguity of this in-between period and to anticipate the new era will be a quantum leap ahead of those who hold on to the past. The time of the parenthesis is a time of change and questioning.

As we move from an industrial to an information society, we will use our brainpower to create instead of our physical power, and the technology of the day will extend and enhance our mental ability. As we take advantage of the opportunity for job growth and investment in all the sunrise industries, we must not lose sight of the need to balance the human element in the face of all that technology.

Yet, the most formidable challenge will be to train people to work in the information society. Jobs will become available, but who will possess the high-tech skills to fill them? Not today's graduates who cannot manage simple arithmetic or write basic English. And certainly not the unskilled, unemployed dropouts who cannot even find work in the old sunset industries.

Farmer, laborer, clerk. The next transition may well be to technician. But that is a major jump in skill level.[1]

Another source found that:

Thanks to automation, the increasing use of subcontractors, suppliers, and temporary workers (many of whom cut, sew and punch data at home), and the reorganization of the workplace in order to provide greater output per worker, steady jobs for good pay are becoming poignant memories or just dreams for more and more people. This is true not only in factories, but in banks, stores, insurance companies, brokerage houses, law firms, hospitals, and all sorts of other places where services are rendered. Between 1979 and 1992, the Fortune 500 companies presented 4.4 million of their employees with pink slips, a rate of around 340,000 a year.[2]

Coping

This coping skill need would center on *relocation*. I had never lived outside a twenty-mile radius of the Springfield area. Family and friends had always surrounded me. This change was remarkable for me when you realize I did it alone and there was the drastic difference in population demographics, square miles and work environment. It was necessary for me to move out of my obsession with privacy and allow strangers to be a part of my life.

The population of the complex was several million compared to around two hundred thousand in Springfield. It was also diverse. When people relocate, new challenges are common. I made it a point to start learning the Spanish language. People speaking that language surrounded me. I had to write the word basura on some of my moving boxes to finally get them picked up with the trash. The phrase, "Do as the Romans Do," suddenly had new meaning. I was living here now and time for me to learn all about the traditions and customs of the Texans.

---

1   Naisbitt, John, *Megatrends* (Warner, 1992), pp. 279-280.

2   Finsterbusch, Editor, *Sociology 94/95,* 23rd Edition (Dushkin, Guilford, CO, 1994), p.162.

4

DOWNHILL TURN:
I MAY LOSE MY JOB

Loss of Jobs

THIS CANNOT BE happening to me. How many people have had this same feeling as companies do their brutal downsizing, rightsizing and transfers. It is humiliating, devastating, and a thousand other adjectives. I kept repeating deep inside that I did everything right: seminars, workshops, higher education, open to travel, commitment. What more could I have done? The railroad had come a long way in their development of women in the workplace. In the past when women married, they gave up their jobs. Later women could maintain their jobs but were not allowed to have any position that might require traveling. Those things have passed, but the railroad is male dominated. I thought I got along well with the male gender, so what happened? The railroad management workforce usually retires after age fifty-five, but I was not there yet. As I learned more about who was eliminated, the pattern started to materialize as though people over fifty had been targeted. This was my first realization that my age might be a factor with regard to my employment. My family disregards age for the most part and continues working and participating in sports long after others give them up.

A human resource representative told me to give up my parking card, business credit card and other incidentals. Since I paid my own parking, this was an outrageous request, and I explained to her I had already paid for the entire month and that I would mail it in when that time was up. She seemed amazed, which amazed me. As the realization was setting in, I knew I had to get out of there quickly because it was evident to me that I might break into a thousand pieces at any moment. Walking down the street, I went through many feelings: shock, sadness, anger, and then I continued to beat myself up as to what I must have done wrong. I was unable to speak to anyone. I just walked. And walked. When I returned to my apartment, there was a message on my phone recorder with a voice laughing and saying, "Bye, bye." I never even knew I had enemies, especially someone who wanted me gone that much. A member of management reminded me that jealousy and envy make people do some awful things to each other. There was going to be a large number of people lose their positions, so some employees were feeling desperate and would stoop to their lowest level. People were going to great lengths at this time to ensure themselves a job. I had the tape analyzed and was so very sorry that I did. I now knew who wanted me gone enough to relish in that information. Sometimes we know more than is necessary.

I could not give up now. I could elaborate on the unfairness or I could make myself feel better and list all the qualified people who were eliminated with me that day. It was evident in the weeks to follow that I was in an excellent company of individuals going through the same circumstance. Why were we chosen? Many of the huge group of individuals bonded together and updated resumes and exchanged job information. We all met each morning at the facility leased by Drake, Beam & Morin so that they could assist the people with their resumes and their depression. Most of the Drake employees had been through some kind of job disruption and were very understanding. The railroad had eliminated so many people that the Drake offices were too small to handle the huge number. The rented facility was just a few blocks from the railroad office complex. This was intended to allow the eliminated employees to feel like they still had a place to go in the mornings, and psychologically, they felt fewer changes would be better at that time. I do not know what is best at a time such as this. I heard people talk about children in college, huge house payments, aging parents and many other fears geared to their own lives. There was no quick and easy course to take to fix it for most of them. I, on the other hand, could go back to a union job in Fort Worth or Springfield, and I had pursued the educational route, so my options were far greater than some of my co-workers.

Loss of job is bracketed with death and divorce as to the destruction a person may feel. In my case, I simply left the management level and returned to a union job. Somehow I knew I should continue paying union dues during the years I was in management positions. I had seen this happen so many times to others. There were a few jobs left in Springfield, and I packed my things and went home.

My new position in Springfield was in word processing. I typed investigations and miscellaneous correspondence. The company had required me to take a typing test before working in this capacity. This was very amusing to everyone when you thought about the positions I had held in the past. This may or may not have been an example of the company encouraging me to resign. There was more to come. Within a few months, the word processing center was moved to Kansas City and we were given the option of going with the job, or accepting some form of early retirement package. I chose to take a six-year reduced-pay package, being paid similar to retirement. After everything was in place, a manager from the Fort Worth office phoned with the information that if I wanted this package I would have to sign a paper negating the lawsuit. This was a new rule and another new decision for me. I told them I could not sign, and to do with me whatever they wanted. I was not paid for several months, and during this period of time I did substitute teaching for the Springfield School District. This turned out to be an opportunity for me to be a part of the academic world, a world I realized that I had wanted to be a part of for a long time. And the experiences that I had in the business world prepared me to better relate business processes and situations.

Some people seem to have periods in their lives when they seek punishment. Approximately a year later I went back to Fort Worth in another management position, wondering what they were up to and why was I setting myself up for more disappointment. Since I was already involved with the group that was suing the railroad for age discrimination, it seemed evident to me that something was up. A very unusual situation occurred when another fellow in my department let me know that he, too, was in the same class action suit that I was in. We did not even know each other. I worked two years at this time with what I assumed held no chance of promotion and very little responsibility. It seemed the more experience and education I achieved, the more menial my job responsibilities had become. In the midst of another downsize, I was sent home again. This time I knew the score. I would survive as I did the first time. It seemed apparent that the company wanted me to disappear.

What was so difficult to rationalize at this time was that I was allowed to participate in a number of team endeavors, traveled to a number of customer locations and was treated as though I was needed. I visited the Thrall Company in Atlanta, and saw our newly purchased gondola-type cars, as they were ready to be sent out of the plant and onto our rail for use. I visited the American Cast Iron Works in Birmingham, and toured the factory and grounds. I was involved with the flat cars we furnished for them to ship pipe. But it was the newly hired corporate trainees who were given the promotions and the higher job titles. The older employees were primarily held to the positions they had been on for a number of years. I also noticed that our employees in the field were rarely given opportunity to fill the positions at headquarters. I still have not been able to understand the rationale behind this type of mind concept. A representative from the human resource department would go to college campuses and recruit people for the manager positions while very qualified, experienced, educated workers would be overlooked time and again. Many of these new hires moved on to other companies in a short time, meaning training costs were high. It is my understanding this practice continues, but I have no way of knowing to what extent.

The present CEO puts out information periodically emphasizing that the railroad fits into the category of a "faith-based" company. We were even told on one occasion that Bible classes would begin soon in the workplace. This did not materialize at our location. Workers here were hesitant at that kind of study when many felt that our company did not fit the faith-based description. Also, there is very little evidence that the union worker is made to feel that they are considered as an important instrument in the operation of the railroad. The fact is that union members make up the highest percent of this particular workforce. I have even considered that most of the problems are a lack of communication within organizations.

During this time period, I had a meeting with the former chief operations officer, who was second to the CEO at the time of the most recent merger between two major railroads, one of which I was employed with, and he encouraged me to stay in Fort Worth and work with a company he was involved in since leaving the railroad. Another offered me the opportunity to manage condos he and another fellow were involved with in Florida and a number of other locations. Other opportunities have come and gone. However, it became apparent to me that I could not break my ties with the railroad. I was like a baby with a security blanket. I have tried to analyze this insecurity and have discovered there are so many branches to our life journey that what looks weak from one standpoint can look like a pillar of strength in another circumstance. It

is not necessary to understand fully the reasons for all tha
Just do something; we must never give up. The ride can be so
rough and rugged, but more change lies ahead. And, just maybe
the ride could even be smooth for a while.

Outside

A study by *Workplace America,* a national publication focusing
on job issues and trends, states that during January, February and
March of 1994 there were 135,000 layoffs, an average of more
than 2,000 for every workday. Here are some of the major job cuts
according to the *Workplace* study:

- **Telecommunications.** Layoffs in this industry accounted
  for 68,300 at six major companies in the first quarter of
  1994 — a figure that represents half of all reported layoffs.
  (In 1994, for example, AT&T cut 16,500 from its staff of
  317,000.)

- **Financial Services.** Six companies were studied by Workplace America; their total layoffs in three months amounted
  to 8,430, of which 5,550 (out of a total of 25,000 employees) were laid off by Fleet Financial Corporation

- **Consumer Products.** The Gillette Company and Bristol-
  Myers Squibb between them fired 7,000 workers during
  that period.

- **Electronics.** At five companies studied, 5,200 jobs were
  lost — Westinghouse, which had 113,664 employees, ter-
  minated 3,400 in the first quarter of 1994. [1]

There are a number of reasons why professionals are termi-
nated in today's turbulent job market. They include corporate
downsizing, acquisitions, company mergers, and layoffs due to
budget cuts. Today it is not uncommon for entire departments to

be wiped out in an eyeblink. Perhaps the worst-case scenario is being fired because of personality conflicts.

When a person is fired, it can be a traumatic experience at any age. One's self-esteem often takes a nosedive. Suddenly one's neat and organized little world comes apart. The amenities one takes for granted in his or her working life disappear. For example, the comfortable office cocoon that confers a measure of dignity, identity and importance evaporates. The convenient office telephone and fax machine are no longer available. The daily camaraderie of fellow workers is lost. Even the convenience of a nearby bathroom is gone. Suddenly you are a man or woman without a company.[2]

From a corporate perspective, downsizing is a good idea. It increases efficiency, cuts costs and enhances profits. U.S. corporations posted large profits during the 1990s, fueling a stock market that nearly tripled in value during the 1990s. After AT&T laid off 40,000 workers in 1996, its stock value increased immediately by $6 billion (Wallace, 1998). AT&T stated that although it regretted the layoffs, they were necessary because of global competition in the telecommunications industry.

Indeed, the increasingly global economy has forced many Americans to change jobs. However, their new jobs often pay much less and provide fewer benefits than their old jobs. Only 24% of downsized workers are able to find employment in the same line of work; about 42% of workers who find new employment are paid less than they were paid in their old jobs (Wallace, 1998). The United States is turning into a nation of service workers. The largest private employer is Manpower Temporary Services, an agency that provides temporary (primarily clerical) workers to a wide variety of businesses.[3]

The era of massive layoffs due to computerization and globalization seems to be over. But downsizing will affect your job prospects anyway. It has eliminated the career ladders that reliably employed large numbers of people throughout their entire working lives, which means you may need to jump from company to company to advance your career. In addition, the skilled jobs available in the private sector of the economy will increasingly involve sophisticated customer service work (for example, financial consulting, hotel and restaurant managing) or the service and maintenance of the massive communications network that has replaced thousands of middle managers. Those who are flexible and capable of doing a wide variety of tasks in work teams may actually benefit from the new arrangements. But they probably will have to give up the idea of regular promotions at a single company or regular and steady increases in pay and benefits.[4]

Apparently the railroads were slow to understand what was happening globally and how they should position themselves to make the transition. Railroads are traditional to this country and a great need exists, but they, too, must make changes. An unidentified source says this about railroads:

"The Law of the Situation" is a term coined in 1904 by Mary Parker Follett, the first management consultant in the United States. She had a window-shade company as a client and persuaded its owners they were really in the light-control business. That realization expanded their opportunities enormously. The Law of the Situation asks the question, "What business are you really in?" When the business environment changes, a company or organization must reconceptualize its purpose in light of the changing world. And now, with situations in constant flux, we must apply the Law of the Situation to present-day businesses.

One business that did not understand the Law of the Situation was the railroads.

We all now know that the railroads should have known they were in the transportation business and not just railroading. It was not so long ago that the railroad industry was the largest in the U.S. economy, and we were celebrating the Pennsylvania Railroad as the best-managed institution in the country. But times changed.

We started to build big trucks and highways for those trucks and then jumbo jets. Even when the evidence was overwhelming that trucks and airplanes were the wave of the future, railroad men (and they were all men) remained, as Harvard Professor Theodore Levitt has written, "imperturbably self-confident." They thought they would go on forever. So did the people who continued to hold railroad stock.

Suppose that somewhere along the way a railroad company, sensing the changes in its business environment, had engaged in the process of reconceptualizing what business it was in. Suppose they had said, "Let's get out of the railroad business and into the transportation business." They could have created systems that moved goods by rail, truck, airplane, or in combination, as appropriate. "Moved goods" is the customer-oriented point. Instead, they continued to be transfixed by the lore of railroading that had served the country so well — until the world changed.[5]

Whether gender differences played a role in my job loss is unanswered. What we do know is that there is still evidence of inequality. Lori Holyfield writes:

> Gender disparities occur in the labor market at several levels, and gender-segregated workplaces account for a significant part. Today women remain highly concentrated in occupations such as secretarial, retail sales, food preparation, teaching, nursing, cashiering and bookkeeping. While these are worthy occupations, the fact that they have been historically female means that they pay less than traditionally male occupations requiring the same level of education and training. Even within these predominantly female occupations, male employees experience more mobility, although the larger the proportion of women in an occupation, the lower are the wages both women and men earn. Indeed, not only are men singled out for promotions

to higher-level positions in traditionally female occupations (most school principals are male, for example), but when they do not seek promotion, they are often stigmatized for not taking a "male" approach to their work. In the end, not only are men and women segregated into different jobs, those differences are unequal.

In almost all occupations, the most powerful positions are reserved for male employees. Women supervise fewer subordinates than their male counterparts, have less authority and fewer decision-making opportunities, and less control over financial resources. In addition, women remain significantly underrepresented at the top levels of major U.S. corporations. Of almost thirteen thousand corporate officers in Fortune 500 companies in 1996, only 10 percent were women. And while women have steadily gained access to professional and managerial positions, the best-paying and most influential of these positions are still reserved for men. For example, women today constitute about 26 percent of all lawyers, but they represent only about 2 percent of partners in major law firms.

Consequently, while education remains crucial — providing the necessary credentials to compete in the job market — pay disparity is equally important. For example, in 1992 women with college degrees earned only $2,000 more than white men with only a high school diploma. When education is held constant, women earn less than men in all categories.[6]

Thomas S. Bateman observed: "Interestingly, the people who lose their jobs because of downsizing are not the only ones deeply affected. Those who survive the process — who keep their jobs — tend to exhibit what has become known as survivor's syndrome. They struggle with heavier workloads, wonder who will be next to go, try to figure out how to survive, lose commitment to the company and faith in their bosses, and become narrow-minded, self-absorbed and risk averse. As a consequence, morale and productivity usually drop.[7]

From another source:

Job insecurity, however, is no respecter of class. In 1991, overall unemployment in the United States jumped 15 percent as companies "downsized" in the name of efficiency and an increase in productivity. But the unemployment rate for managers rose 55 percent. As the organization of the world's work shifts, more and more of us, from waste-basket emptiers to CEOs of multinational corporations, are waking up to the fact that we are swimming in a global labor pool.[8]

Coping

It seemed to me when I lost my job that all statistics and studies were in error. I had pursued education, training, experience, and had worked with enthusiasm and nothing protected me. This coping skill would need to be centered on *loss*. I tried to concentrate on the positives in my life, kept myself very busy, and tried to remember many others were feeling the same way. But the sense of unfairness was so overwhelming that I wanted to see that this kind of activity was stopped. There are a number of books dealing with loss, but I have found most people have to discover what works for their own individualism. Crying is not an outlet for me, but it is a good cleansing for many. Others turn to addictive behaviors such as eating excessively. Others seek counseling. We know overeating answer, nor are the other addictive behaviors. They just d the problem. Good friends came to my rescue again. usband took me to Memphis.

Perhaps Dennis Whaley says it best:

"Failure is an event, not a person."[9]

---

[1] Bernbach, Jeffrey M., Esq., *Job Discrimination: How To Fight ... How To Win* (Crown, New York, 1996), pp. 5-6.

[2] Connor, J. Robert, *Cracking the Over-50 Job Market* (New York, Plume, 1992), p. 30.

[3] Bradshaw, York W., Healey, Joseph F. and Smith, Rebecca, *Sociology for a New Century* (Pine Forge Press, 2001), pp. 2-3.

[4] Ibid, p. 427.

[5] Naisbitt, John, *Megatrends* (Warner, 1984), pp. 87-89.

[6] Holyfield, Lori, *Moving Up and Out* (Temple, Philadelphia, 2002), pp. 68-69.

[7] Bateman, Thomas S. and Snell, Scott A., *Management Competing in the New Era,* 5th Edition (McGraw-Hill Irwin, New York, 2002), p. 283.

[8] Finsterbusch, Editor, *Sociology 94/95,* 23rd Edition (Dushkin, Guilford, CO, 1994), p. 162.

[9] Wholey, Dennis, *The Miracle of Change* (Pocket Books, New York, 1997), p. 218.

5

FACING THE DECISION
TO FIGHT BACK

The Lawsuit

MY HUSBAND, JASON, and I were on our way to Memphis to see a lawyer. The entire development was surreal, and truly I was seeing it as though it were happening to someone else. You can be assured I never dreamed I would have the confidence to bring an age discrimination suit against a Fortune 500 company. For one thing, I had read too many mysteries and I would expect to be blackmailed and all my years of service discredited during the process. My mind would not even allow me to examine the facts at this moment. That had all been done prior to this time. I seemed to be functioning out of my body, as though from afar. It seemed my mind had compartmentalized itself as if some aspect of mind control was at work. This was not the case. I was literally on my way to visit with a lawyer.

The appointment was scheduled for one hour. We met with one of the new attorneys and gave him a complete overview of the situation. He phoned the senior attorney we were supposed to be meeting with and asked him to join us. We spent the entire afternoon talking about the company I was working for and what had transpired to cause me to want to bring forth an age discrimination suit. I was told that I had a strong case and that I would be added to a group of other employees who were filing a class action suit against the same company that I worked for. I kept thinking about a statement I had heard somewhere about, "Go hand in hand with others, so you can pick each other up as you fall." Was I expecting to fall? One of the members of this group had confidentially told me what precipitated the class action suit and that they needed me to help them fight this blatant show of disregard for their older employees. Things were beginning to come together, and soon I found myself on an emotional roller coaster; yet it became one of the most interesting experiences of my life. More changes and challenges were imminent.

It was my understanding that the lawyer I had retained was determined to support the working class employee and that he had handled some very high profile cases. In fact, he was known for being steady in his pursuit of fairness to workers. He assisted on some of the air traffic controllers' cases and appeared to have the problems of the "little guy" on his heart. He wanted all of the information I could furnish as to numbers, dates, positions, etc. There were a number of people within the corporate arena wherein I worked who mailed me information anonymously, and many were willing to just hand it over. I'm sure they were aware of the reduction of older workers within our company and felt that the information they were providing would somehow benefit them in the long run. The assaults on the older workforce were so blatantly handled that even many younger employees saw what was ahead for them if things continued in the same pattern. In fact, many of them just quit for other work opportunities.

The day I was "let go" was emotionally traumatic and an assault to my very being. All I could think about was trying to determine what I had done wrong. It made no difference that co-workers were supportive of me, as in my current state of mind I did not hear them reaching out to me at all. For a few days I obviously experienced what was probably a deep depression. Nothing really reached me and my thinking was veiled. I believe my behavior was normal on the surface, but I am convinced that when people feel they are assaulted or betrayed, and they do not understand why, it takes time for the healing process to occur. Studies indicate that loss of a job ranks with death and divorce in the mind traumas. I was working in the finance department, responsible for the engineering department's budget. Our team worked well together and there were no complaints. My performance evaluations had been very good. I enjoyed the job and tried to give total commitment to it. Why did this happen?

When I could function in a positive state again, I phoned the Equal Employment Opportunity Commission (EEOC) in Fort Worth. They would not talk to me and told me that the company I worked for was a good company and that I did not have a case. They would not even listen. I then phoned the same agency in Dallas. Their take on the case was quite different, and they told me to get all the information together and mail it to them as soon as possible. I complied, and in the meantime I was required to exercise my seniority. Subsequently, I found myself back in Springfield. After a considerable amount of correspondence, the Dallas EEOC agency mailed my papers to the St. Louis agency and both offices advised me that from the information provided, I did, indeed, have an age discrimination case. Their workload is huge and even though they would take the case, due to time constraints, they suggested I proceed with an attorney and pursue the case.

My visit with the attorneys in Memphis appeared well worthwhile, and I was included in the class action suit being pursued by other employees within our corporation. Now the long wait would begin. I went to a union position in Springfield, then back to a management position in Fort Worth for another two years. The lawsuit proceedings continued, and subtle and not-so-subtle situations occurred in what I perceived to be an attempt to try to persuade me to quit. I could not quit; that would be giving up too much at this point in time. Our company had just recently gone through a merger with another corporation, and there was a complete "changing of the guard" within the senior management staff. It appeared there was no direction and corporate policies were continually changing. The former management team with whom I worked consistently encouraged me to pursue a higher education. I listened to their advice and took college courses at night. I received a master's degree and a doctorate degree as well. Now, in my current situation, for example, even with my education and experience, I was never considered for promotion. This was a striking contrast to all my prior years at headquarters. On the contrary, I had been asked to apply for positions on several occasions.

It is important to state at this time that upon my return to a management position in Fort Worth, my co-workers were excellent. None of my peers seemed to know about the lawsuit or what had happened to me in the past. I traveled to several locations for job-related meetings and was included as a member of the team. It was strange, but expected when I was found to be in a downsized group again. This time there was very little depression and no questioning on my part. I felt I knew the reason. I went home again to Springfield. This time I would work at the terminal where train operations take place. This work environment would open new challenges, entirely different from those I had encountered in a corporate office. How many more changes would I be expected to make?

Just when it appeared that nothing would ever happen with the class action suit I was party to, I received a notice telling me that a date had been set for depositions. It had now been approximately five years. At one point during this process, my attorney suffered a heart attack and did not practice for approximately a year. Depositions were taken in Fort Worth, at the law offices of a very large and prestigious law firm located in the beautiful Bass Building. This law firm taking the depositions was retained by the company that I worked for. I had been told that the railroad was using this firm in addition to their own staff of attorneys due to the fact that under no circumstances could they lose this case and allow it to make the news. It would seem that there had been such a blatant practice to furlough older people that they must spend any amount to squelch this from becoming public. As I was not privy to their reasons, much of this information would be speculative. We were now down to six people in our class action suit; the others had all given up. We were deposed individually, and that would prove to be one of the most exhausting experiences of my life.

My attorney, the railroad-retained attorney, a court reporter and I started the process. The impressive, elegant office complex several stories up would have been intimidating to most people, but I had already been awed by the big office building I had worked in for several years. The questions asked during the deposition started, becoming hard and fast. My energy levels plummeted as the stern, arrogant attorney interrogated me throughout the day. He started with my youth and attempted to make things I said have a different meaning. He especially tried to make something of the fact that my husband lived in another state while I worked in Texas. I wondered why my lawyer did not stop this type of questioning since it did not seem to relate to the work situation at all. The thought flashed through my mind that real life is not like the movies. He kept hammering me about my personal life until I finally asked him why he was so interested in what I did outside of work rather than my work life. He laughed at me. It was finally over and my lawyer advised me that I did well. I was now so drained that it was difficult to negotiate the elevators and make my way to the car. Jason was waiting for me, and we made the eight-hour drive back to Springfield. The big question I kept repeating to myself was, "How did I ever get myself into this situation?"

Within a few weeks a similar proceeding occurred in front of an arbitrator, my attorney, the railroad attorney, the railroad-retained attorney, and me. The arbitrator was experienced, and my first impression was that he would be able to see the unfairness of this situation. All of the participants in the case had agreed to "binding" arbitration with no chance of a trial. My lawyer suggested we go ahead with this, since a trial date would take years to secure. The railroad witnesses came and were basically very respectful to me. In fact, they gave no reason at all as to why I was in the group selected to be downsized. My lawyer produced no witnesses, as he said our documents proved what happened. The two people who took my former management position did not have either the experience within the railroad nor the amount of education that I had. The documents proved both employees were in their thirties, one female and one male Hispanic. It appeared as though the retained attorney enjoyed trying to make me look "little." It also seemed he talked down to me as though I were of no value to this company at all. He made me feel just the way he probably planned. I was the lowest I had ever been. I wondered if I would be able to walk out. When the session was over, the actress in me took over, and I was able to pull out conversational skills and actually visit with my perceived enemies. The retained attorney even asked me if I was acquainted with an attorney he knew in Springfield. They appeared concerned that I was making the eight-hour drive back home that night. I have come to believe that we all play a part as though we are in a play a great deal of the time. He was simply doing the job he had been trained to do.

I received a letter from my lawyer advising me the arbitrator ruled that three of us had been discriminated against and three had not. The finding in my case was that I had indeed been discriminated against on eleven charges. I had won. Two weeks later I received a call from my lawyer saying it was the hardest call he had ever had to make. The arbitrator had reconsidered, with no reason given, and said that I had not been discriminated against after all. I was not surprised. By now I knew how the game was played. The binding was only for us, not the railroad. From what I know, there is one fellow still in the case. A judge is reviewing the

:ause there is evidence of improprieties in the han-
arbitration. I wrote a letter to this judge giving an
hat I knew, but as of this time I have heard nothing.
Money and position equal power. A person steps into a huge nega-
tive arena when attempting to question that power. I questioned, I
lost, or did I? A form of change is to be aware and question that
which does not appear to be right. I have no regrets about my part
in asking why alleged unfair practices occur so frequently in big
business. The railroad spent huge amounts of money to an outside
law firm and many hours of their own legal department to win
their case. What made it so important? We could have been given
a little money and sent on our way, completely out of the company. Maybe we did win after all.

This chapter is not meant in any way as an exposé, as I feel no
great anger at the railroad. On the contrary, the railroad has given
me a great deal. Whether it is the job I wanted or not is beside the
point; I have always had a job. They paid for three educational
degrees and many seminars, workshops and travel. I have been
given a wealth of experiences, and during every adventure I have
always learned something new. Support and respect from fellow
railroaders at all levels far outweigh the opposite. But good and
evil are apparent in our lives, and we must discern the difference
in high decision-making circumstances.

Outside

You know you have done a good job … but somehow, you
weren't promoted or given a raise, or worse, you've been fired.
Maybe you were too old or too pregnant, or a member of the
"wrong" sex, religion, race, or ethnic group, or disabled by illness
or a physical characteristic. Maybe your boss or another co-worker
sexually harassed you and made your life miserable. If any of these
(and other) descriptions apply as reasons why you suffered work-

place discrimination, you may be in what is known as a "protected category," and as such, you have a federally mandated right to seek justice in the form of getting your job back, receiving that promotion, plus compensatory, punitive, or other (financial) satisfaction for what may have happened to you.

→ What identifies you as "protected"? The definitions are established in Title VII of the Civil Rights Act of 1964 (usually referred to as Title VII), which prohibits discrimination in employment based on race, color, religion, national origin or sex. The Age Discrimination in Employment Act of 1967 (ADEA) prohibits discrimination on the basis of age. The Americans with Disabilities Act of 1991 (ADA) prohibits discrimination based on an employee's disability.

↘ However, being in a protected category is not all it takes to determine whether you have a prima facie (basic) claim of employment discrimination. To proceed successfully under Title VII, the ADEA, or the ADA, you must be able to answer four questions in the affirmative:

1. Are you in a "protected class"? In other words, are you a minority, or over age forty, or suffering a disability, or was your sex, religion or national origin the issue?
2. Were you qualified for the position in question — either to be hired for this job, or for a promotion, or not to have been fired from your job?
3. Did you suffer an adverse employment decision — such as not being hired or promoted, or were you fired?
4. Did the situation occur under circumstances that could be interpreted as a discriminatory action? For example, was the company's "reason" for doing what it did untrue, and was the job in question given to someone substantially younger, or of a different sex, race, or religion, or someone who lacked your particular physical disability?[1]

Coping

↗ This could be identified as *loss amplified* when determining the coping skills required should you find yourself discriminated against. The ride you are on may take a severe turn, and you as the engineer must do some expert handling in order to stay on course.

---

[1] Bernbach, Jeffrey M., *Job Discrimination: How To Fight ... How To Win* (Crown, New York, 1996), pp. 15-16.

6

REASSESSING MY GOALS

Hanging On

MY OPTIONS WERE few. I needed to work a few more years to secure my retirement numbers. My attitude was most important at this stage of the process. I would be working with people who had nothing to do with any of the negatives. It was very important to remember that problem situations tend to stay with us much longer than the happy ones, and my new co-workers were in no way involved.

The union jobs available to me were located in two areas, and it became evident that the best option for me was a midnight driver, commonly referred to on the railroad as a crew hauler. On a resume a person might refer to the position as a transportation specialist. Whatever name the job is given does not make any difference; anxiety was creeping in again. I have come to understand in the life journey, whatever experiences one lives through will assist in the next one, but there will always be a certain amount of fear. Our culture has taught us to rely on fear in religion to do what is correct. This carries over into all the other areas of career, family, and day-to-day living. If we do not conform to a set of norms, then bad things will happen to us. I felt I had always tried to do what was the "right" thing, and still some very bad things happened to me in regard to my career. Now, as they say, it was time to pick up the pieces and start again.

Working the night shift proved interesting. My body wanted to sleep so badly during the hours from four to six in the morning. My co-workers told me I was in a trance; I do not know, only that I could barely function for that period. It would seem that the melatonins were asleep. The people were great. A railroad group becomes a family as they struggle with the lack of rest, irregular hours, large numbers of them never knowing when they would be called to work, layoffs, and much more. I was later told that many of my immediate co-workers did not think I would be able to work in this environment. My work history would have seemed to them one of privilege. They were very wrong, as I became connected with the operating personnel and can truthfully say this period of my railroad journey has been one of the best. It is perceived that senior management has very little understanding of the educated, enduring, resourceful group of operating employees. If only they could somehow penetrate through that wall and reach an understanding instead of seeking out any problem areas and concentrating there. It was immediately evident that safety initiatives were being used as disciplinary measures, which, of course, negates the whole purpose of a safety program.

I was involved with the safety initiatives when they were put in place. The railroad spent several million dollars to bring the DuPont Company on board to develop what they deemed necessary for railroad workers to be able to work in a safer environment. Protective equipment became a way of life, and mandatory drug testing was in place. We all complain about it, but overall, the program has, hopefully, saved lives.

Working nights allows a person to view the world from a totally new perspective. My first experience watching lightning dance across the sky sent chills through me as the incredible beauty was intensified. The moon was glorious as the slim shape slowly grew to its full size. It became evident why so many legends and religions came from this magnificent specter of beauty. I could understand the energy levels associated with it. Whether this has anything to do with moving with change I do not know, I can only relate as to the beauty and serenity associated with the nighttime sky. I believe this experience allowed me a greater understanding of my spiritual growth, as well as physical understanding of the nighttime worker.

Then came the opportunity to work afternoons. This time period has a new set of problems and concerns. A person will miss anything done in the evening. Parents miss school activities, and spouses miss those special Friday or Saturday nights together. I felt a lot better physically, but both family and friends related more than once that these were terrible hours to work. Spiritual growth continued during this period, as I was with some co-workers who were deep into trying to understand where they were in this capacity. One person opened up some of the Eastern beliefs and how that thinking had brought him closer to an understanding as to why some drastic family situations had happened to him. Another one would open up the thinking well past organized religion to true spiritual awareness influencing me to open my mind further. I also read many books on the political far right movement, aliens, and government secrets. I had studied about the secret societies for a long time, and it was mind-boggling to find people who had the same awareness, only intensified. My mind was suddenly open to a thinking that I had always held captive due to religious fear. One of the most interesting aspects of this time period was that all of this information did nothing to dampen my beliefs, but only widened my thinking to accept more possibilities. I was changing in a number of ways.

There were other interesting aspects in getting to know the train and track operating personnel. We had one fellow on a Tulsa crew who always came in with a smile and would sing us a song or two. Sometimes we would join him in a song. I can see him in retirement as an ambassador using music as the international language. I worked with an artist skilled in making pictures come alive, a golfer who excelled, a man involved in professional horse racing whose hobby enabled him to get to know some very well-known entertainers, and many other fascinating interests. There were a few female employees, but predominantly my co-workers were male. I am sure it was as entertaining for them as it was for me as we managed to bridge the gaps in the male/female viewpoints. I took a three-man crew to a fast food restaurant one evening when they were working at a power plant away from the terminal and needed a meal break; they found it very amusing when I ordered a chicken *sandwich* with no bread. That form of ordering a low-carbohydrate meal had not occurred to these fellows. It would appear that we were quite a conflicting collection of characters.

This particular time period of work hours allowed me the opportunity to see undomesticated animals becoming almost tame. I watched a family of foxes as the parents went about teaching the four youngsters to grow up. They played in an area between the railroad tracks and a brush-filled ditch. It was very close to trash bins and numerous old buildings filled with rats and mice. They were a delight to watch. I could drive my van within a few feet of where they were playing and there was no fear of me. I also saw raccoons, deer, wild turkey, and a number of other forms of animal life when going into the power plants to pick up crews. If this job was engineered to be some sort of punishment, then something went askew; it was filled with adventures.

Operating personnel must learn early in their careers how to adjust the scheduling, families, and all that relates to these issues with a constant ability to meet changes and learn to be flexible. I was no exception. I found it was true that my career had been one of privilege and ease compared to the people I now worked with. Even though I had a few major disappointments in my career, which ultimately seemed to stop my career for the railroad, most of my years had been spent in very positive situations. It takes a great deal of determination to stay with a company if you are made to feel unwanted or unappreciated.

The rumor mill continued with talk of more job cuts and lay-offs. There was a bill before congress that would change the full retirement birth date to sixty instead of sixty-two. Railroaders are very resourceful, and a number of groups went to work. Retired people who had a little more time lobbied and worked diligently for us. The National Association of Retired & Veteran Railway Employees (NARVE), unions and many current employees would find themselves writing, phoning, and taking ownership of the responsibility as to how the congress votes on such issues. I understand the age sixty had been in place until the railroad employees voluntarily gave it up to allow the government to take our money and use if for a national need. This had passed long ago and the economy allowed us to regain the sixty-year retirement age. The bill passed easily through the House of Representatives, and the president assured us he would sign the bill. The Senate turned out to be another story. Senators Phil Gramm (R-TX), Pete Domenici (R-NM), and Don Nickles (R-OK) tried every way possible to stop the bill and were successful for a time. Senator Trent Lott (R-MS) would not allow the bill to come up for a vote, so the session ended with no vote at that time. I want to add here that Senator Domenici does vote for the laborer on most legislation. Things have a strange way of working out for the laborer sometimes. One of the senators changed his party affiliation, becoming an independent. This move took Senator Lott from power, and our bill was allowed to come up for vote. The bill passed by a huge margin, and the railroad laborer was given back the ability to retire at sixty. We, as a group, had just proven that working together we could make change happen. The bill would allow me an earlier chance to reevaluate how to spend the next chapter of the change process.

During this period of time I allowed my mind to wander into any avenue it took to establish what my next move would be. I talked with strangers that I would meet at Barnes & Noble in regard to what kind of books they liked to read and what interests they had. My friends in Texas used to go on incessantly about how people talked to me everywhere we went. Whether that was true or not made no difference; I was now taking advantage of any ability I might generate to talk to strangers. I was led to do this, and never once considered it as anything but normal. It was simply time for me to investigate and to understand if this meant I was to get to know a stranger before moving forward. At this time, I still do not understand the need to search; I just know that it is necessary.

I knew I wanted to be a part of the academic world, and I also knew I wanted to help others as they struggled with how to make decisions and how to fit into society as unplanned predicaments came their way. It had become necessary for me to help people understand that it is a true statement when people relate how bad things happen to good people. I had seen this happen so many times that I could not stand by and let people feel that they were somehow always to blame for the disappointments that came to them along the journey. We all have a responsibility to ourselves to let go of the baggage and move to the next chapter. More changes were coming on the ride.

Outside

Richard Bach wrote in *The Adventures of a Reluctant Messiah:*

"The simplest questions are the most profound. Where were you born? Where is your home? Where are you going? What are you doing? Think about these once in a while, and watch your answers change."[1]

Dudley Lynch and David Neenan write:

> As a change agent, you can no longer authoritatively point out the train on the tracks — the Makeover or Reengineering Express — and let it leave the station without you. Not if you are to make the journey, enjoy the experience, pocket the benefits, and revel with everyone else in the excitement of becoming and achieving and contributing.
>
> This time, we understand we are mostly dealing with a world that is being generated from the inside out, not the outside in. A world in which every participant is a reality-maker. A world where a new understanding — and appreciation — is developing for the role of the observer and for the skill of observing.[2]

They advise:

- Being persistent in your efforts to learn and grow.
- Being perpetual in your willingness to change — your quest to become what you can become.
- And, being perennially committed to your search for fundamentals — for elegant underpinnings to shore up your abilities to roll with the surprises. To perform well in the midst of the challenges. To restore and renew your abilities to participate on yet another day, no matter how tough the new issues, trends or unanticipated developments.[3]

Coping

The dominant coping skill necessary at this point in my career centered on *change in direction*. Decisions were becoming necessary before I had time to properly evaluate the prior one. I had to determine if my career in business was over, if my career in teaching was beginning, and just what direction did I want to go. I read somewhere that the only one who's happy about change is a wet baby. It is so difficult.

---

1 Bach, Richard, *Illusions: The Adventures of a Reluctant Messiah* (Delacorte, New York, 1977), pp. 46-47.

2 Lynch, Dudley and Neenan, David, *Evergreen* (New Echelon Press, Lakewood, CO, 1995), p. 28.

3 Ibid, p. 29.

7

SHARING THE MESSAGE OF CHANGE

The Future

THE NEW PASSAGE in my life has begun. The fear and anxiety have been replaced with excitement and new things to do. Many people have crossed this road from many years in the traditional workforce to early retirement or to a new type of work. Most of us cannot even believe we are in an age category that opens this type of decision-making. Where did the time go? The time has come to face the next chapter. I have decided that I do want to share my experiences with students and direct them to get aboard the ride of life with an attitude to take the risks and see what life holds for them. Some of my friends advised me to spend my time traveling and take life a little easier. It sounds good, and I am doing that, but travel with no purpose could bore me quickly. Others suggest writing a book for people who are facing significant changes in their lives and might be comforted to know how someone handled their situations. As you can see, I have decided to do the writing. All of these suggestions and more have crossed my mind and caused me considerable confusion. The railroad has been like a good/bad relationship all these years. It is like a child carrying a security blanket around. It may be dirty and ragged, but it is familiar and, therefore, comfortable. I know the company may appear dysfunctional in some areas, but I have been inside so long, I understand the dynamics. Leaving has opened up new guidelines and questions. And leaving was one of the most difficult things I had ever done. How long must I prolong and dwell on the unpredictable future? I knew it was time to rationalize and peruse some serious avenues. After all, few important decisions are made instantaneously, and all my decisions did not have to be made immediately, but my personality is one that cannot remain dormant for very long. Something must be going on. So I knew that it was time to examine the possibilities.

I went into a jewelry store recently and decided that was where I wanted to work part-time. Immediately the customer walks into beautiful surroundings with lovely merchandise, low lights, soft music and a very relaxing atmosphere. The sales associates are helpful and friendly and seemed to know the products and services very well. Jewelry has a long history, and I felt I could get into the current market scene. I started to rationalize how I could learn the country in which the product was mined, how the markets got the product, distribution, and the markup scale. It was laughable really, since it was not necessary for me to be an expert as a part-time employee. And, what about all that education that I worked so hard to achieve? Do I use it?

When we received information that the railroad was offering an early retirement package, my mind started churning regarding what I wanted to do for the next twenty years. I decided to check out the jewelry store as a job applicant. I took my résumé in and asked for a manager. I dressed in my black suit in order to look professional. The butterflies came back, and I wished I had mailed it instead of bringing it into the store. I knew I had absolutely no sales experience. The security guard advised me the manager would get there at noon and that I could come back then.

Surprisingly, I did take the résumé back and asked for the manager. She came out; I briefly told her who I was and handed her my résumé. She told me they were full-staffed right now, but would keep my résumé on file. We visited briefly and I went on my way. It was not so difficult after all. No big, bad wolves out to get me. The big question was why I even thought these things. I then asked myself why did I think someone would be mean to me because I wanted to work for them. The rationale made no sense at all.

I also spent lots of time in the Barnes & Noble book store, and I started thinking about working there. Again, the atmosphere was excellent with the inviting smell of coffee and being surrounded with so much information and knowledge. It was becoming a game with me as I tried to figure out the number of authors located in this one store. And authors always give credit to other people, and so I also tried to add them to my number. Business, art, romance, spiritual, the list goes on and on, and they were all there. My associates, which were the books, could be very good friends at this stage of my life as they had been in my childhood. I could just get lost in there and stay for a long time.

And there was the Peace Corps. This had been in my mind since high school when the call was made to all of us to "serve." I had several interviews and put this one on "hold." Family needs held this at bay as I realized it was necessary for me to be home now. A person makes a two-year commitment, and I would not want to start something that I could not complete. This could still happen in the future.

Regarding the classes that I am currently teaching for a local university, I have found to be such a joy just to have the opportunity to share information with those on the road to their higher achievement. My friends and acquaintances are from a wide variety of chosen walks of life, and I find a person can excel in so many different areas. But for me, higher education allowed me the room to grow in self-confidence and it also broadened my scope of understanding. A person is not necessarily smarter, just has a grasp of a larger dimension. Well-read people can develop a similar scope by being exposed to the unknown and achieving an understanding of information through words. Whatever source is open to an individual for seeing a broader picture of the universe, it is my firm belief we have the obligation to ourselves to capture and use the message. My classes allow me the opportunity to know and share with my students. I feel with certainty that I have a place in the academic world. But something kept telling me that I have more to do. As I examine different avenues of place, I feel the answer will come to me.

It may be the book. I have known for a long time that I wanted to try my hand at writing a book. Remember the old enemy called fear. Every time I mention or even think about my book, fear comes marching in. And I thought that old enemy was conquered. Guess not, because every kind of excuse keeps coming to mind. What will I write, who will publish, who would read what I had to say, and on and on with excuses. But the story keeps coming to mind anyway. I went through some wonderful experiences and dragged myself through some disappointments. It is evident to me from many acquaintances that others have traveled the same road and will do so again. Maybe one little piece of information as to how I handled my situations will give strength and comfort to a struggling person.

One day I started writing and could not stop. My love affair with words gave this project great excitement. I hope professors will assign it as a read along with the textbook. Things happened to me in the business world, and I was forced to regroup and take another road. Looking back, it was not so bad.

I allowed a few friends to read certain portions of what I wrote along the way as words turned into sentences, then paragraphs, to pages, and now this. One comment I often heard was: "Your words reveal how you kept soldiering on." This was the assurance I needed.

Outside

The United States is expected to add about 18 million jobs by the year 2000, about 1,000 to 5,000 a year. If you know what you want to do and where you want to work, you are ahead of the game. If you are still uncertain about what to do, look at the jobs that offer the best opportunities, keeping in mind new and exciting occupations, jobs that don't exist today, will be created as we move toward the twenty-first century.[1]

U.S. Department of Labor data indicate that the United States is becoming a predominantly service-oriented economy. Manufacturing represents only 12 percent of all jobs. People without high school diplomas are at a distinct disadvantage, because their employment opportunities are becoming confined to the lowest-paying service jobs. Even lower-skilled occupations of the future will require workers who can communicate well and read and comprehend instructions, and have a working knowledge basic mathematics. For example, the job of assembly-line worker traditionally was considered a low-skilled occupation. Today many of these workers are learning statistical process control techniques, which require a solid foundation in mathematics.[2]

The baby-boom generation (born between 1946 and 1964) is aging, which will cause the average age of the workforce to increase to around 40 by the year 2005. The number of people age 50 to 65 will increase at more than twice the rate of the overall population, and by 2008 over 16 percent of the workforce will be 55 years of age or older. At the same time, the number of younger workers (ages 16 to 24) is expected to drop to 16 percent in 2008.

As a result of these trends, the Bureau of Labor Statistics projects that entry-level workers will be in short supply, and fewer new workers will enter the labor force than will be lost through retirement. Many older employees are opting for early retirement even though there is no longer a mandatory retirement age and life expectancies have increased. Companies therefore need to retain and hire older, experienced workers.[3]

A significant decrease in the workforce would lead to less tax revenue and income for federal programs, such as Social Security, economists say.

"That's something to be concerned about with the baby boomers," Mount Holyoke College economics professor Michael Robinson says of the generation that is approaching retirement age. "If the labor force participation rate gets too low, there won't be enough money to pay those funds."[4]

The Administration on Aging reports on workers of the future as follows:

With increasing numbers of older adults staying in the work force, the trend toward early retirement is beginning to reverse itself. Many older adults believe that the higher levels of education they possess will allow them to continue making unique contributions to society. Other older adults will continue to work because of economic necessity. Many older workers are among the 17% of older Americans who have incomes of less than 125% of poverty.

The 1999 U.S. Department of Labor study, "Future Work: Trends and Challenges for Work in the 21st Century," reported "the new millennium promises opportunities" and "creates risk." Employers and employees now face challenges in the way work affects their lives and livelihood. A 1997 Radcliffe Public Policy Institute study projects that the number of workers age 45 plus will reach 17 million between 1994 and 2005. The study, which focuses on training older workers, noted that as we move into the next century, "Neither employers nor employees can afford to sit by as the skills of the workforce become obsolete."

Aided by the observations of researchers and policy makers, and by contemporary experiences, employers are becoming more aware of the value of mature workers. Old myths and stereotypes are fading. Today, the knowledge and skills most in demand are those necessary for positions in high technology and the service industries. Because of the changes wrought by technology, there is a diminishing supply of jobs that require sheer physical strength, which is more often a requisite for jobs in manufacturing and the heavy industries.

Recent studies show that intelligence and productivity do not necessarily diminish as people age. The ability to learn remains constant throughout most of the life span. Like any other part of the body, however, the brain functions optimally if it is continually stimulated through use.

The future world of work is being shaped both by our demographics and by emergent technologies. The criteria for participating in the twenty-first century workforce is evolving. Today, many new skills are required by jobs in the growth industries. Among other factors, the actual acquisition of new skills will determine individual roles in the workforce.

The repetitive functions of traditional manufacturing jobs are becoming obsolete. Today's just-in-time production demands just-in-time workers — i.e., skilled, contingency, part-time or temporary workers who can be hired on a moment's notice to fill a moment's need.

The Department of Labor's National Industry-Occupation Employment Matrix projects a 14.4% increase in the number of jobs for all industries between 1998 and 2008.[5]

One source, speaking of schools for the twenty-first century, states:

The public education system as currently structured is archaic. It cannot reform itself, nor can it be reformed by even the most talented chief executive. Trying to do so would be like trying to convert an old-fashioned linotype machine into a word-processor; it can't be done. They perform the same function, but their methods and technologies are so different that one cannot be turned into the other. Instead of a school system that attempts to impose uniform rules and regulations, we need a system of schools that is dynamic, diverse, performance based, and accountable. The school system that we now have may have been right for the age in which it was created; it is not right for the twenty-first century.[6]

Coping

What does all this information mean to you and me? Based on the information available to us, it appears we will be able to find a job for as long as we want to work. The statistics reveal we need to be as mathematically sound as possible, able to communicate effectively, and willing to be a change agent. The phrase is back. We are shifting from industrial to technology and service. To make adjustments, it is necessary to be open to learning additional skills. In my opinion, whatever our background circumstances, to secure and build on a satisfying career, we must be open to education, training, and staying abreast of happenings in the global economy. The coping skill necessary is to understand that we are dealing with the *unknown* and to treat such as an adventure and not as a fear.

"Only in growth, reform and change, paradoxically enough,

is true security to be found" (Anne Morrow Lindberg).

And as John F. Kennedy stated: "Change is the law of life. Those who look only to the past or present are certain to miss the future."

---

1   Connor, J. Robert, *Cracking the Over-50 Job Market* (Plume, New York, 2002), p.19.

2   Bateman, Thomas S. and Snell, Scott A., *Management Competing in the New Era,* 5th Edition (McGraw-Hill Irwin, New York, 2002), pp.353-354.

3   Ibid, p. 352.

4   *USA Today* Careers Network — More men just say no to working (Internet, 9/13/02), p. 3.

5   *Employment and the Older Worker* – Administration on Aging Fact Sheet (Internet, 9/13/02), pp.1-2.

6   Finsterbusch, editor, *Sociology 97/98,* 23rd Edition (Dushkin, Guilford, CO, 1994), p.196.

SUMMARY

FAMILY, FRIENDS, ACQUAINTANCES and a number of circumstances account for much of the insight and tolerance I have learned. Even when I may view what another person says or does as strange or wrong, I try to wait a moment and consider that I am not that person and have not walked in their footsteps. My students always hear me talk about "in the box." For some of them, it takes several weeks into the semester before they start to understand what I am talking about. Then, at some point, they start to explain what the phrase means to them. For some, it is leaving family traditions, for others working with people who are different, and for others seeing new ways of doing things. For all of them, they start to understand thinking out of the box is opening their minds to greater understanding. They do not want to function in a closed atmosphere. Even if opening up to new ideas may bring a certain amount of uneasiness, it also brings challenge and opportunity. It can be very uncomfortable to walk a path that no one you know has walked.

I would hope that my walk, and the walk of the people profiled, might bring some insight as to the importance of accepting the changes that happen to you in a more positive light. They can be VERY frightening, as well as exciting. Living away from my husband, family and friends, moving to a big city alone, seeking higher education, working for higher level positions in the workplace all constitute fear of the unknown. Communication has enabled us to be aware of so many things in the world to bring us anxiety. We know just enough about health issues, weather concerns, nuclear/ chemical concerns to keep us in a state of unrest. For me, it is best to try to know all that I can, and then just secure the information in my internal file cabinet and take it out when needed. It is important to dwell very little on the negatives that happen to us, move away from those thoughts as quickly as possible, and pursue the positives.

I have saved what may be the best for the remainder of my book. I interviewed some very special people who by choice or by outside design made drastic career changes or growth processes along their individual journeys and this is a brief profile of their stories.

Hop aboard for a ride with some very interesting individuals.

Coping

Change has become the prevailing life mode; a life rooted in constants seems a thing of the past. Social change complicates life by shifting standards, values and behavior patterns. It also increases friction between groups, and within groups. When change is especially frustrating or upsetting, the question of coping with it becomes of paramount importance. Coping is required in situations of drastic change that defy familiar ways of behaving and require the production of new behavior or new responses.[1]

Embracing change is to embrace life. Resisting change is to embrace death. Rigidity is death-like. Flexibility is vital to living and growing. We only need look to nature to find that this is true. The rock is hard and rigid, yet the flexible sprout of the tree will split the rock in its compelling struggle for life. Following the wisdom of its seed, the sprout knows no fear or failure.[2]

---

[1] Vago, Steven, *Social Change,* Second Edition (Prentice-Hall, NJ, 1989), p. 345.

[2] Oliver, Gene, *Life and the Art of Change* (LifeChange Press, Costa Mesa, CA, 1999), p. 59.

CHANGE PROFILES

Profile 1: Peter Riola

IT IS NECESSARY to understand Peter from the time he was a little boy. His Episcopalian mother, Sara, had married Bill, who was a Roman Catholic. She had agreed to sign a document that children born to them would be reared as Roman Catholic. The couple had three sons and did, indeed, educate them in Catholic schools and trained them in the traditional Catholic doctrine. Peter's mother was even named Roman Catholic Mother of the Year at one point, due to her participation in the church and school. Peter's mother was the primary source of spiritual guidance during his youth. What was interesting to note regarding this achievement was that she was still an Episcopalian, never having gone through the necessary steps of changing her church affiliation. During this period, Peter was very close to his maternal grandfather, Ralston Hewitt, and attended church services with him at the Episcopal Church on numerous occasions.

Peter did well in school and received the religion medal every year. Upon completion of high school, Peter applied to the Roman Catholic seminary in order to train for the priesthood. His application was declined with the explanation that he attended two churches, both the Roman Catholic and the Episcopal, and he apparently was not focused enough on the catholic belief system. Whether these same guidelines are in effect today, Peter does not know, but that was the situation in the fifties.

The Episcopalians gave him no grief about the situation, so he stepped across the street and began his studies at the Episcopal seminary. But this career was in question. He was a young man now and needed an income. He started looking for a job.

He accepted a summer job with the railroad in New York City, and that summer job would become a career that lasted thirty-seven years. He started as a mail clerk making thirty dollars a week, promoted to file clerk making forty dollars a week, then to senior clerk making fifty dollars a week. He was making some money and liking the way that made him feel. What an important passage it is to feel the independence of being on your own. We all know how significant that is to our self-esteem. He made the decision to go to college at night and work during the day. The seminary would have to wait. He weighed the decision alternatives and felt this was right for him. During this period, he was able to complete three associate degrees, get married and have a family.

He worked for nine years in this manner moving up the ladder. At one point he was offered a better paying job with another company, but he knew that if he stayed with the railroad for ten years he would be vested and eligible to draw railroad retirement. More decisions to be considered. He stayed where he felt there was a certain amount of security due to the family responsibilities he had to worry about. Other job possibilities came and went; one offer came after working for the railroad nineteen years with the same choices. The new offer sounded so enticing, but if you complete twenty years with the railroad, retirement benefits improve again. He stayed.

The family grew up, his personal life experienced some major changes, and he was still completing educational pursuits. There was the bachelors, the masters, and the doctorate, now what should he do with these accomplishments? He was still with the railroad and had made moves from New York City to Philadelphia, to Buffalo, and now he was being moved to St. Paul, MN. Most of his management positions within the railroad had been in sales and marketing capacities; now he was going to become involved with development and training. This position would be at the director level, and he would be doing some very interesting things as he worked with people in the development of their skills and encouraging them to surge forward in striving to reach new levels. Now Peter is experienced in the organization and function of the railroad, sales and promotion, and developmental training.

The railroad was involved in mergers and acquisitions and ultimately determined headquarters to be in Fort Worth. Peter and his wife, Martha, made another move, this time to Texas.

Within a very short time, the downsizing, rightsizing, extreme changes would be happening to the railroaders. Peter went into his office to find an early retirement package on his desk. His first thought was that, "I am not going to give up this salary." He went home and told Martha the news. Her first remark, "Are you crazy? The railroad is going to afford you an opportunity to pursue the ministry." She had realized immediately that this was his chance to have the time again to pursue the priesthood that he had always wanted to do. They talked a great deal about this decision and what it would mean to them. She knew how much he did at the church as a lay person and how his heart was there. He knew it, too, but the security of the salary coming in was very hard to give up. Pension benefits were good, but nothing to compare with working. Deep in his heart he knew the railroad wanted him to quit because he was fifty-five years old, and people rarely stayed in management positions after that age. He signed the papers to retire. As it turned out, his position was abolished, and three people in the twenty-five to thirty age bracket did the work he had been solely responsible for. He recalled how he had looked around at the last meeting he attended and he was the only one with gray hair. It was time to make the move from the railroad to something new. Change agent was looming; he was aware that many decisions had to be made.

His first job after retirement was director at the Senior Citizen Center. Everyone appeared to be significantly older. Peter designed senior activities programs. He then took the job of chaplain for Hospice. That area of work also helped him to get over the hurt of the railroad job loss. He estimates it took him a year to fully understand the feelings and hurt associated with perceived job disappointments. He was also now able to understand that his job changes were simply growth changes and an opportunity to do something else. The railroad had trained him well and provided all the educational pursuits he needed.

He knew now that it was finally time to pursue the goal he started such a long time ago. What difference did it make that he was now hovering near sixty? It was time. He and Martha moved back to St. Paul where Peter was made bishop and executive vice-president of a college. The decision had been made and everything seemed to be falling in place. It was an exciting and fulfilling time.

Peter is now the bishop over the whole diocese of 40 parishes, making his home in St. Francis, MN. He goes to Oxford University in England for a number of weeks each year to study and teach. He is a fellow in philosophy at Oxford. He has finally come home in a number of ways.

What would this story have to do with a business student in today's environment? Peters' story exemplifies the human instinct to stay in the safety of a routine paycheck. Circumstances prevent most of us from taking the risk-taker route. He learned many things during his time in the business world in regard to dealing with people issues. This type of training would serve him well in the ministry. He also learned organization and how decisions are passed down through the various levels. His experience with people enabled him to have a strong foundation in human resources. He felt he was better prepared to go back to his original career choice.

Had he become a priest in his very young years, his entire life would probably have held a different story for us. Change agent was probably not a common phrase to him, and risk-taker was another popular phrase of the future. Job availability and the need of an income was the most apparent reason for Peter to board that railroad a number of years ago. He gained much from the ride and is now sharing and growing in a totally different capacity. We have the opportunity to sit back and see what comes next. I am sure it will be stimulating to watch.

Outside

Today's universities have their origins in the institutions that developed in eleventh- and twelfth-century Europe. They began in Italy, spread to Spain and France, from there to Germany and Scandinavia, then to England, Scotland, and finally America. The contemporary American university is an amalgam borrowed from western Europe, particularly England and Germany. The assumptions underlying the undergraduate curriculum originally came from England, whereas graduate education is grounded in German scholarship and science. The English influence can be dated from the founding of the first college, Harvard, in 1636. The German influence did not take hold until more than two centuries later. The curriculum was designed to produce a learned clergy and cultivated gentlemen and to impart an aristocratic lifestyle to the well-born. In the seventeenth century more than half of the college graduates became ministers, and most college professors were clergymen, or at least were trained in theology. Prior to the Civil War, almost all the college presidents were ministers.

In the early American college the principal method of instruction was *recitation*. This is a process in which students repeat from memory, often verbatim, textbook assignments. (Remnants of this method are still found in Eastern European and Soviet universities.) For *disputation,* students defended or attacked a proposition in Latin, the required language of instruction. Later on, the lecture by teachers supplemented student recitations. Because of the limited number of books, students often copied down word for word what the instructor said. As the size of classes increased, the lecture method slowly replaced recitation and disputation. The blackboard was first used at Bowdoin College around 1823. The *seminar method* was imported from Germany in the mid-nineteenth century. Finally, the *discussion class,* designed to supplement lectures, was introduced at Harvard in 1904 (Boyer, 1987:149).[1]

Profile 2: William H. Holmes

IT WAS MY first meeting with William Holmes. Dr. Holmes it is now, but it was not the profession he had initially planned. His career began in the field of teaching. His expertise was coaching. What happened to change his mind?

Bill was a student at the University of Kansas and playing basketball. Lawrence, Kansas is a basketball town with a history of excellent coaches and strong community support. Larry Brown, who would later move from the college level to the pros, was coaching him. He started to realize there was more to coaching than the average coach understood. The Division I school was so good, so scientific in the teaching of the game. He knew he could teach the game. He changed his major to Physical Education and completed his degree moving in the direction of sports. He felt he understood the game better than most new coaches and wanted to put what he had learned to use.

He started his coaching career in Missouri, first at Morrisville where his team won a state championship the first year. He then coached at Nevada and Rogersville. He loved the game, but as in most professions there are many additional factors to consider.

Coaching is very political, and a person can be very popular at one moment, especially with a winning team, and quickly find himself at the other end of the spectrum if events do not quite meet expectations. One coach told him, "Don't plan to be any place longer than three years; people will turn on you." He kept saying to himself, "I have a family and I do not want to move around because I have lost my job, out of some political confrontation." He kept feeling the lack of respect directed toward education and educators and knew he was capable of fighting some battles, but not this one. By this time, the whole atmosphere was beginning to feel very wrong for him. He started asking himself if he was in the wrong profession and contemplating what he should do. He was in his thirties and wondering if he was too old to formulate a drastic career switch.

Those of us growing up in the Springfield area come to realize that we stay naïve in some aspects, and Bill found that coaches did seem to be naïve about a lot of issues at this period of time. The unrest was building. He stayed in the coaching profession from 1981 through 1988.

During the middle '80s it seemed that the educational field was taking a dynamic turn. Discipline was out. If a teacher dared to discipline in a way that might be deemed as too severe, then there was a price to pay. To the teacher. During the era in which Bill grew up, there was strong support for the teacher with parental backing. The parents usually enforced the disciplinary measures of the school, and the students knew this. Respect for the teacher, the school, and the parents were expected. Changes were happening at a fast pace. Paddling was out, time-outs were in. Communication through the television media was instrumental to some of the changes. More subtle forms of changes were creating a new forum of educational thinking. During this era, educational practices were in an almost total reverse. Disciplinary actions at the school would bring the parents into the school, angry and demanding. Most of the parents of the '80s children were born as products of the '60s whose parents lived through the period in history filled with unrest, Viet Nam, the assassinations of John F. Kennedy and Martin Luther King, racial disturbances, the resignation of Richard Nixon, all played a part in this significant change to the culture.

These kids were offspring of a real change in society. They were taught to challenge, not to just say yes or no. At times they seemed to rebel even when there was nothing apparent to question. Education was caught in an unstable change mode. Bill liked to teach and he felt gratification in helping to enhance someone's life through education. There was that yearning to be of assistance in making someone better. All of these issues were relevant as to why major changes were happening throughout the country.

In education today, problems fester and it seems nothing is resolved. Bill was becoming very disillusioned with his career and knew he needed to identify the choices available to him. This profession was no longer fulfilling to him. It was time for a major change.

Bill now had to assess the choices open to him and how it would affect his family. He had a wife and three children. His father was a doctor, his mother a nurse, so he had been exposed to the world of medicine. His physical education classes were health-related, he held a masters degree in education, and so he examined how those backgrounds could start the process of a new profession. His father suggested medical school. He examined the possibly of becoming a nurse. He kept feeling like he was too old to change careers. He was still in his 30s, but our cultural norms have made us feel that we should be set in our professions long before this age. This mentality almost made him sell himself short. But he persevered. He started medical school.

The family learned how to budget time; it was very important for him to be able to be a father and husband. He went to the contests, recitals, games, and managed to develop impressive management skills. The free time to relax and play with his family sometimes required him to study all night. But he knew it would not last forever, and he did not want to miss the growing-up of his children. The second round of school took four years. His wife worked, his parents helped, and the student loans enabled him to complete this endeavor. His parents, as did most people of their generation, saved in advance to attain what they wanted. It was necessary for Bill to step out of that mind-set and meet the challenges in the best way possible.

It takes time to become a doctor. In our microwave world of instant gratification, this entire process would prove to demand personal commitment and a strong goal-oriented personality. Everyone in the family was affected, hopefully not negatively. It was expensive; he started in 1988 and the student loans will not be paid for two more years.

The choices were not over. The question now haunting him was what direction he wanted to go within the medical fields. He knew he did not want to deal with chronic conditions in which there is no fix. He really wanted something that he would see a positive change in people and happiness in the conclusion. He realized medicine must spend a great deal of time on aging, death and dying. It was almost an oxymoron, how he was adamant in pursuing a positive profession and yet there was so much sickness.

He identified the field of medicine as appropriate to his needs. Optometry. There is very little death and dying involved. Eye conditions are usually treatable, and the treatment is quick compared to most conditions. This was the type of environment he wanted in which to practice his skills.

Upon completion of medical school, there were still decisions and choices to deal with. He could have more security related to financial income in a commercial corporate situation. The paycheck would come with certainty every two weeks. But he had already become a risk-taker by changing professions in his thirties, so now he was becoming an entrepreneur. He opted to go alone in this venture. He opened his own office three and one-half years ago. He is the only physician in the facility and employs two assistants. He has concerns, but knows this was the way to go. How much advertising and where? Hire another physician? The questions go on and on. But the questions do not have to be answered yesterday. He has made concentrated changes and pursued to conclusion. Nothing ventured, nothing gained, was one quote he expressed to me. This physician has embraced the role of change agent in a most positive way. Interviewing him enhanced my viewpoint that there is no stopping those who possess the incredible drive to make changes for themselves as well as mankind in general.

Outside

I read a number of articles on teacher statistics and studies. This survey was done during 1994 and 1995. Some interesting information follows:

> Twenty percent of former public school teachers and one-third of former private school teachers were employed elsewhere. Among teachers who left the teaching profession between 1993-94 and 1994-95, 25.7 percent of public school teachers expected to retire, while 24.1 percent of the private school teachers expected to work outside the field of education. Among public school teachers who left between 1993-94 and 1994-95 and cited dissatisfaction with teaching as a career, student discipline problems (17.9 percent), poor student motivation to learn (17.6 percent), and inadequate support from administration (15.3 percent) were cited as the main reasons that they were dissatisfied with teaching as a career. Among private school teachers who left between 1993-94 and 1994-95 and cited dis-

satisfaction with teaching as a career, lack of recognition and support from the administration (30.2 percent), poor opportunity for professional advancement (14.6 percent), and inadequate support from administration (12.5 percent) were cited as the main reasons that they were dissatisfied with teaching as a career.[2]

Profile 3: John

JOHN IS AN attorney. He has no intention of changing his career. So why are we looking at him as if he is a change agent? After all, this book is about change and how to deal with it. It has become clear to me as I interview people and write their stories that very few people are exempt from change. The society we live in today requires that we be open to constant change and growth. Our nation left the agricultural and industrial ages long ago and has moved full force into the information/technology era. To succeed, don't we all agree we must stay tuned for our next leap?

John is very busy with his clients, and that is his career priority. He and his partner of fourteen years have a general civil practice. A large part of their practice is counsel for insurance companies whose clients have had auto accidents and need representation. But that is only one example; their practice is inclusive of all types of litigation. John spent his first four years in Springfield as a public defender before going into private practice. He is intuitive to the needs of people and Springfield. His openness to new ideas requires him to consistently open doors. Those interests have led him to investigate other opportunities of learning.

He, his wife and two sons live in a historical part of the city and participate in the preservation and rebuilding of the area. They own some rental property in the area as well. As a youth, he would help his grandmother in making repairs to her rental property. His father had a very strong work ethic. Creative skills, interest in preserving, and financial insight could all have been developed during this process.

John serves pro bono for the Sherman Avenue Project Area Committee in which the focus is on rehabilitating property for the low-income people. He also serves on the Urban Neighborhood Alliance Coop, which targets blighted spots in the center city and seeks grants for the repair and restoration.

He has served on the Landmark Board whose responsibilities cover the changes to historic property. Some of these interests have caused him to want to understand more about the architecture. So he is taking architecture classes at Drury University. This could also be an outlet to fulfill his creative instincts. He reluctantly admitted to me during his first class in drawing that he received the A+ that the teacher had challenged the class to achieve. She had told the class in the beginning there would be only one, and John achieved that goal.

Educators, parents and many others continually pursue the secret to motivating young people to excel. There are a number of good ideas and plans, but it seems to be a combination of circumstances that cause people to continually seek higher learning. It is interesting to go back to John's family to understand what makes him want to keep learning new things and enhancing the things he is already involved with.

John described his parents as non-traditional. His father started college already having a wife and three sons. He had started immediately following high school, but decided that was the wrong path for him, quit school and joined the Marine Corps. Now it was time to go back to school and finish what he had started. The term change agent is starting to appear in this family and will be evident many times through their children.

John's mother was a secretary and assisted with the family finances during this period of time. In his twenties John's father was selling lawn mowers at Sears and realized this job was not for him. He enrolled in St. Louis University, finishing with a degree in commerce. He finished his master's and took a teaching position with a community college as his first job. He would work his way up to dean of vocational education. He was working on his Ph.D. when tragedy struck this young family and he was killed in an auto accident. His mother had started college when John was thirteen years old and received her degree in education. She would also pursue a master's degree. Following the loss of her husband, she had to assume the responsibility of her young family.

John's older brother owns his own plumbing company in Washington, Missouri. He, too, made some interesting decisions regarding his education and career. He dropped out of high school, moved out of the family home and joined the army. We can only imagine how this decision affected his parents, who had become so conscious of educational pursuits. While John was attending Missouri University, his brother would get his GED and complete his education to receive a college degree. He took a different route but did achieve the goal.

His younger brother owns a resort in Kimberling City, Missouri. Prior to that, he was a property claims adjuster. As we are starting to understand, the members of this family are diverse and appear to be open to a number of opportunities. It is always interesting to know the family. The similarities and the differences just prove that we are all very individualistic.

John finished high school, went to college, earned a business degree, then went to the University of Missouri for law school. He felt comfortable in the planned course he wanted his journey to take. Even though the career choice was one that John had wanted and worked for, he would use his change agent skills in other directions. He had decided not to live in the St. Louis area where he had grown up because he wanted to establish his own independence. Columbia, where he completed law school, did not seem right for him either. Springfield was the place he chose to practice law.

He married, and at age thirty he and his wife had their first son; four years later their second son would complete the family. They decided to live in the center-city area, which was very untraditional for most young families. John understood that if the downtown area were to be preserved, it would be necessary to participate in a number of ways. His wife shared his enthusiasm. She worked in public relations for the Ozark Area Community Action Corporation (OACAC).

John's sons are busy with school, and both of them play on club soccer teams. The boys are the number one priority, and the family devotes whatever time is necessary for their needs.

Does anyone question why I would ask him to assume a role as "change agent" in my book? He is all about change and growing. His active mind will not rest. There is always something new to discover and something else that needs to be done. This person exudes with enthusiasm and motivation.

Profile 4: Nancy Berlin

NANCY WAS BORN in Riverton, Wyoming. Her father worked for the Corps of Engineers, and she had lived in twelve states and gone to six different high schools by the time she graduated. Eight years were spent in the Silicon Valley area. Contrary to what you may be thinking, she came from a very stable, traditional family. The family placed a high emphasis on God, and that guidance has remained with Nancy throughout her ever-changing and always growing life.

She married at age eighteen, and a year later had a little girl. Her husband, who was older than she, was already working on an accelerated degree program at the University of North Colorado at Greeley. His degree was in fine arts. They lived in the student housing area, and Nancy stayed with the baby. Decisions were coming to this young couple, and they decided he would take a job in Tulsa, Oklahoma. He took a position in retail advertising with Dillard's Department Store, headquartered in Tulsa at this time. He had some yearning to be a columnist or do political cartoons, but that is hard to penetrate, so this avenue seemed right for him. He had secured his teaching certificate, but did not have the true desire to teach. This move put Nancy in a new location and some decisions of her own. They now had two young children to care for.

Women were breaking barriers in big numbers during the '70s and '80s. Nancy was no exception. She took some courses in library science, but soon found that was not for her. She also took some classes in legal terminology at the University of Tulsa, but she soon realized she wanted a job. She was in her early twenties when she went to work for the Williams International Co. It was 1974 and Williams was involved with petroleum, and OPEC was the word of the moment. It was very exciting. Transacting business with all these international expatriates, host-country nationals and third-country nationals would advance her knowledge extensively. She started as a secretary in the international division for the treasurer. She soon found that she understood numbers. She was not intimidated by them as so many people are; they just made sense. She also found that she enjoyed working with people and public speaking. She very quickly became the assistant treasurer. Nancy still had not completed her degree, but she took night courses, soaking up the information like a sponge. She continued learning at her job as well, handling million-dollar transfers from Nigeria and Oman. She was becoming very detail-oriented. There were no computers on every desk; communicating was done through writing and telephone, commonly using interpreters. It might be necessary to conduct a twenty-million-dollar transfer with Nigeria, which was in a police state. It was fascinating! And she was learning constantly.

She rode the bus to work as most people did who worked downtown because parking spaces were limited and this was the most convenient form of transportation. The company she worked for was located in the Bank of Oklahoma Building, so very large and important. The children went to daycare and school, this being difficult for women, but becoming necessary for so many. They stayed in this location for three years.

Another move was on the way. Her husband was being transferred to Fort Worth, Texas. The Dillard's company was moving headquarters to Fort Worth, and he would have to move. They bought their first home while there, but stayed in this location only one year. What was Nancy going to do now? It was evident already that her mind must be active and involved with something. She started her job search and became involved in another type of career. She took the position of project manager for a housing development company out of New Jersey. Her background in finance got her the job. When her dad retired from the Corps, he became a vice-president of U.S. Homes, a housing developer. He was a wonderful resource for her as she learned her new line of work. This position would give her experience in housing, construction, development and financing. This job was proving to be interesting and the foundation for many types of work in the future.

Then more changes. They had been in Fort Worth only a year when her husband took a position with Wal-Mart. He was moving them to Bentonville, Arkansas. The plan was to stay there. They bought a home. Nancy could stay at home with the children and do some work from her home. She did some bid estimates, plus advised on procedures to secure financing. At age 28, she decided to go to work full-time. Again. Another start at her career.

She looked back at her educational classes geared toward library science and knew she was not made to work in a library or teach. She looked at her experience and her resources and pondered what to do. Women were so often viewed as secretaries only, and this time was no exception. She went to work as an assistant to a vice-president over lending in a bank. She threw herself into learning: real estate, commercial, consumer, and construction finance. After six months, she had an assistant of her own. She always went to school in one way or another: training sessions, seminars, courses geared toward what she was doing. She requested permission to go to Jonesboro for a two-week training course. The bank wrote a personal letter, and Nancy was accepted to the intense, accelerated program. The course required an extensive testing process to complete. Of course, she completed the program. When she came back, she was promoted to assistant vice-president. She was primarily involved with commercial loans during this time.

She was also becoming involved with the community, as head of the Business Development. She worked for the very progressive Walton Banks (now ARVEST Banks) for five years. Here she was able to overcome several of the obstacles common to women in the workplace.

Then it hit. Her husband announced that he needed to leave Bentonville. This ultimately meant her personal life was taking an extreme twist. But at this moment, she would do as he wanted. She finished a Certified Financial Planning Course, which was very intense, about this time. They headed to Springfield, Missouri. Why Springfield? She had given careful consideration to a few places, with the final decision resting between Santa Fe, Boulder and Springfield. She had toured Great Southern Savings & Loan once and was very impressed. They did not know one person in Springfield. But her life had been made up of moves, requiring meeting new people and starting over. This was just more of the same.

Now where would Nancy seek employment? We know! Great Southern. She went to work there and they were good to her, but it just wasn't where she knew she needed to be, and she would soon move to Commerce Bank as a vice-president in May of 1987. She stayed with them for over seven years. During the '90s she became very involved with the community. It was becoming apparent that she could communicate effectively and it was enjoyable.

Her husband moved out of the house the day after Thanksgiving. Nancy acknowledges that she probably knew it was coming. But everything changed abruptly, and she was suddenly a single mother and facing new decisions and problems. She had expected to stay married forever as a traditional family. This personal change in her life would be instrumental in the professional life that she was to pursue.

She was still attending classes and gaining experience and knowledge. While at Commerce, she became involved in the area of health care finance. She was instrumental in the development of a medical model for Commerce. This would network her to healthcare personnel such as physicians, assistants and administrators.

This association was helpful in her being recruited by St. John's Health Care System to work in the workers comp area. This business required her to go into companies in the Missouri area to assist and train companies to handle workers comp. The managed care discount, work place accident prevention, return to work decisions, and a huge financial burden on a company requires extensive knowledge. She trained and assisted the companies in how they should respond. The financial emphasis is huge in workers comp, and it is imperative that it be handled properly. Nancy went to seminars and learned all she could. She was able to observe carpal tunnel procedures and became familiar with diagnosis codes, risk analysis and third-party administration. She had been in finance for six years, but this was a new dimension. She was now becoming proficient at outcome measurements: did the patient get well, what were risk behaviors, and how many returned to a productive existence? This was a high-growth period.

But more changes were ahead. She had served as a volunteer for the victim center and had subsequently been invited to serve on the board. This gave her an opportunity to become acquainted with a new avenue of business with a wonderful way to help people in need. And, as you might guess by now, she was invited to be the executive director.

She contemplated the career move and realized that if she decided to assume this new responsibility, she would have now made three major career changes: from banking to healthcare to a crisis center. How did this happen? She was supposed to be at home raising a family — not in the workplace arena at all. Instead, she has been moving and growing as a professional every step of the way.

The Victim Center is an agency that depends on funding from a number of sources. As director of the agency, Nancy spends a considerable amount of her time securing funds to meet the needs of the Center. In addition to being a member of the United Way, private donations and grants are necessary. But even though Nancy is responsible for the business needs of the organization, she is most concerned about the victims who call on them for assistance. Members of the team are on call twenty-four hours a day and will go to a police station or hospital at any time when called. They are trained to help a rape victim, as well as other forms of victimization.

Change agent she has proven to be, there is no question about that. I hesitated to ask what was ahead for this ever-growing woman. She smiled at me and indicated that she was where she wanted to be in regard to a career. But she is starting a program to get a bachelor's in criminal justice. She has never had the time to finish her degree, and the time is now. She will be doing most of it via Internet classes due to her busy schedule. I am sure that she is focused enough to pursue this method of education. She and her second husband, Bob, are discussing a move to the country, and just maybe, some horses. With all the structure of a career, she believes it is so very important to add a hobby or two. Unwind, laugh and enjoy. Her spiritual focus was evident throughout our visit. She does not go alone.

Outside

It is interesting to point out that in the early '70s OPEC was becoming a household word for Americans. Prior to this time, most of us had not been aware of the Middle East to any great extent. Nigeria joined with Iran, Iraq, Kuwait, Saudi Arabia, Venezuela, Qatar, Libya, Indonesia, United Arab Emirates, Algeria, Ecuador and Gabon to form the alliance. The governments of Saudi Arabia and Venezuela issued a declaration on May 13, 1960, recommending that petroleum-exporting countries pursue a common policy in order to protect their rightful interests.[3]

Coping

When hard decisions hit this young woman, she took her natural high-energy and drive and went to work. Planning, decision-making, evaluating all came into play. And her strong spirituality gave her the will to want to move forward.

Profile 5: Paula Gott

PAULA HAS NOW moved into what would appear to be the best passage of change to come her way. She has progressed through many changes and feels they were all important to reaching the specific goals at the time. But this one, how special! She is an author; she has experienced enough life to make the romance with words come alive on paper so that we can all share in the adventure. Even as a child, she would look out into the universe asking for answers. Sir Isaac Newton was one of her favorite people. She always remembered one of Newton's three laws of physics: "For every action there is an equal and opposite reaction." She was fascinated by how similar that statement was to one made by Jesus and frequently quoted to her by her mother: "Do unto others as you would have them do unto you." Her mother always added, "That means, what you give is what you get!"

The moon and the sun fascinated her: their light, their circles through the sky, the many cycles in nature. In spite of the experiences of a sometimes-dysfunctional childhood environment, she always felt that the future held something very special for her. She loved to write stories, and her mother encouraged her to excel, to try new things, to reach new heights, and not to permit any limits to be placed on her.

But life held some detours. Paula did not finish high school in the traditional way. Instead, she had a husband and one child before she was out of her teens. Although it took several years to accomplish, she was determined that she would change that. At the age of twenty-nine she took the GED test to get her diploma equivalency, and then she enrolled in college.

In 1972, now with two children, she signed up for nine hours of college credits. She attended school in the mornings while her youngest child attended kindergarten. She arranged her class work so that she would arrive home before her daughter, just fifteen minutes, but she managed to do it.

During the second year, she carried twelve to fifteen hours. Her youthful marriage was finally over in 1973, and more changes and decisions were waiting. She knew she would have to drop out of college and was very disappointed. She stopped by the office of an acquaintance on campus to tell him of her decision. Bob Peace was director of business operations, and his response was quick and firm. "You can't drop out of school. How will you support those two kids?" Her meek answer had something to do with "waiting tables." He marched her down to the financial aid office and explained to the counselor there, "We have to find a way to keep this young woman in college." She signed up for student loans, grants, scholarships, anything available that would pay tuition, buy books, and cover living expenses. She applied for work on campus and utilized all the avenues available to her in the pursuit of this goal. With the help of many caring people on campus, she graduated in four years in 1976 with a degree in business education. Ten years later she went back for a degree in psychology.

While on campus, she met many interesting and influential people in the field of education. Bob Peace insisted she not give up on her goal of receiving a college degree. Neva Maddox Johnson would be a role model; Paula worked as her student assistant; Tom Fowler, Dean Don Calame, and others would all play a part in her growth.

Tom Fowler, her business law instructor, had given her a grade she felt was lower than she deserved. While both were waiting to speak with Neva Maddox (he to ask for help in finding an office assistant; her to ask for help in finding a job), Paula finally voiced her displeasure at the grade she had received from Fowler. By the end of the conversation, he had offered her a job and she had accepted. Neither needed to see Neva Maddox after all.

Most of her duties in Fowler's office consisted of general office work in the preparation of wills and other legal documents. But she would also research cases for him to use in a class he taught to pre-law students. This turned out to be an excellent opportunity to learn how to maximize the use of the library, to search Missouri statutes, and it planted a seed of interest in women's issues that continues to grow today. She would find controversial cases, about half dealing with women's rights — or lack thereof. One case dealt with whether a man could be charged with raping his wife. Fowler finally told her to please find some cases other than all those liberal women's and sex cases. The conservative lawyer and the liberal feminist student agreed on practically nothing politically or philosophically. But both recognized in the other a person of integrity and character, and there is still a standing offer of a job — as long as the salary demand is within reason.

After graduation she taught school one year. She found the students to be disrespectful and the pay too low. Teaching would not provide for her needs after all. She sold real estate for a couple of years, and in the late '70s she found herself once again working for Tom Fowler, who was now a bank president, as his secretary. That position didn't provide enough variety or challenge, so in 1979 she took a position with a construction company and worked there for a number of years as regional field office manager. The company headquarters were in Seattle, Washington, but Paula worked in Midwest field offices in Springfield, Missouri, Harrison, Arkansas, and Houston, Texas, with a short stint at the home office in Seattle. She remained with the company for the next ten years, with occasional interruptions. She also remarried, but retained the last name she had carried for twenty-three years — Gott.

In 1986, she was again ready for a change but not certain of what she wanted to do. She signed up as a Kelly girl and was assigned to an insurance company and third-party administrator as a temporary secretary for the owner. She was offered a full-time position as secretary, but rejected that offer. Two months later she was called back and offered the position of "claims supervisor." But first, she had to learn about health insurance claims, so she was trained to adjudicate claims. She remained in that position for eighteen months. During that time she found numerous inefficiencies in the claims processing system and offered suggestions, including fuller utilization of the computer and streamlining of the handling of claims. She negotiated a pay increase based on the increase in production and settled into a career in the insurance industry. She progressed from claims examiner/claims supervisor to claims manager, and finally in 1992, to vice-president of operations. But this was during the time of acquisitions and mergers, and in 1995 the company was sold to a large national HMO that employed over 20,000 people. It appeared to her as though the company's methods were steeped in greed, and both she and her boss were very uncomfortable with the new philosophy of "profits before people." The driving force behind virtually all decisions was increasing the stock price. People were laid off, a freeze was placed on hiring, and serving the customer wasn't even on the list of goals.

Her boss, the executive director of the division she worked for, decided to try to buy his company back. There was significant evidence the HMO did not want him — or her. They could never agree or comply with the philosophy and tactics of the HMO. But that is another story; this one is about Paula, our champion of change.

How many changes has she gone through now? She has touched banking, construction, teaching, insurance and higher learning. All this in addition to short fill-in jobs and significant changes in family situations. She is now a grandmother. But once again, something was stirring deep within Paula. She had been paid a nice salary — with substantial bonuses from time to time — and had saved enough money to be able to examine what she really wanted to do at this time of her life. In 1999, she made the agonizing decision to leave the security of a well-paying job to set out in search, again, of her purpose in life

The old desire kept returning: "I want to write." She believed that through writing she might be able to fulfill the other lifelong desire: "To make the world a better place." With change there is almost always some discomfort. She had encountered some disappointments and some wonderful experiences. The reason was becoming quite clear. The experiences would enable her to share with others in the very special form of writing. Her mother had stressed the golden rule, and Paula looked to that from time to time as her affirmation tool — along with Newton's law of action and reaction. She used what's known as "treasure mapping" and kept a journal, writing down the things she hoped to achieve. She reviewed her goals and dreams daily, and then left the way to achieve them to be revealed to her.

She was now out of work and writing a book, but there was still more to come. Her husband, Joe, had semi-retired, so time constraints were no longer holding them to one location. They bought a motor home and took a position as winter caretakers at an RV park in Taos, New Mexico. Life became even more interesting. Paula's personal goal was to take this time to get physically in shape, lose weight, and allow her mind to meditate and look for guidance.

One day during her morning walk, she stopped at a little church to meditate and to see what guidance might come to her. There was a beam of light shining through the window that seemed to be focused on one of the pews. She sat in the ray of sunshine and waited for a flash of understanding to be revealed. It didn't happen. So she found herself using the time to ask for more patience, to have a more loving disposition, to be kinder to others, to be more generous, and to be a better listener. She knew she could use improvement in all these categories. She promised herself that she would start by being a better person, and then focus on what she could do for others. Maybe then the guidance would come.

As she walked along the road back toward the RV park, she saw a panhandler walking toward her. He had the ragged clothes, unshaven and unkempt appearance, and a slow, sorrowful demeanor. Her first impulse was to cross over to the other side of the street and avoid the encounter. But suddenly, in her mind, a voice simply said to her, "What if it's Jesus?" Knowing Paula as we do by now, what she did was all that she could do. After all, she had just sat in a church and promised to work on being a better person. She walked up to the man, looked into sad blue eyes and smiled. They began to talk, and he told her about his life, of spending most of it in mental institutions. And then he asked her a question: "Do you know what 'messianic ideation' means?" He added, "That's the diagnosis they pinned on me." Then he smiled, and his eyes glistened. He held her gaze for a long moment, and then said, "But I'm not crazy."

He then asked her if she could give him fifty cents for the bus so he could get downtown. She was dressed for walking, she carried no purse or billfold, but she reached into her pockets and felt some change. She realized she had two quarters in each pocket. Another message popped into her head. "If they ask for your coat, give them your cloak also." She handed the beggar the fifty cents for the bus and then gave him the fifty cents that was in the other pocket. He gave her a gentle hug and they parted ways. But the impact of that encounter was to become one of the major turning points of her entire life.

Another unusual experience transpired while she was in Taos. The woman who owned the RV park needed to be away for a couple of weeks and asked Paula to take care of her living quarters and her Great Dane. There was no television in the large apartment over the park office, but the walls were lined with bookshelves crammed with books. Of course, this was not necessarily unusual; what was interesting was that the subject matter was Paula's longtime interest, physics. Sir Isaac Newton had been joined by Einstein, Bohrs, Planck and many others. The woman, whose last name is Latin for "Light" and who had a Ph.D. in physics, spent summers running her RV park in Taos, and winters in San Francisco working as a quantum physicist. Paula read about the history of physics, quantum physics, and string theory. At about the same time, she saw an article about "The Jesus Seminar," and ordered two books that came from that group's work, "The Complete Gospels," which included the gospel of Thomas and the gospel of Mary, two ancient texts that didn't make it to the New Testament. Her mind was now intent on merging science with the New Testament, and what she found as she studied physics alongside the

New Testament astonished her. The numbers in the New Testament, especially the book of Revelation, can be directly linked to what modern science says about the formation of matter and the formation of the Universe!

Later, when they were back in the Springfield area, the Don Imus Radio show mentioned they needed a manager at the ranch in New Mexico. Her mind started racing. Why not? She sent her resume to the ranch, they sent it to New York, and she had started the process to get herself hired. One month later she was called to New Mexico for an interview with the Imus's. Before she left the ranch, she was told she had been hired.

So she and Joe were off to New Mexico. The ranch was established as a not-for-profit corporation to provide an experience for kids suffering with cancer or other blood diseases, and for siblings of victims of SIDS. This was, she believed, her chance to make the world a better place for a bunch of kids who had been given one of life's most fearful and perplexing challenges. She realized fairly quickly that the number of children who were given the opportunity to visit the ranch was quite small — about sixty each year. Many of them returned year after year, keeping the total number of children served even lower, and each child spent only one week at the ranch. She was disappointed but had to acknowledge that this was not the "cause" and life's work she had hoped for. And she was able to validate a long-held suspicion: All the money in the world is no guarantee of happiness.

But the New Mexico ranch experience brought many new friendships, and New Mexico has now become a second home.

When asked if there was a moment when it all began to come together in terms of her own fulfillment, she was quick to respond. "The moment I felt my heart turn from 'What will I get from this?' to 'What will this do for someone else?' The true change in my life started with the 'Jesus experience' in Taos when I began to consciously try to treat each person I meet the same way I would treat them if it were Jesus. The more I do to help others, the more joy I experience for myself. The money and the 'stuff' it bought provided a fleeting sense of pleasure, but true joy — ecstasy — a continuous sense of fulfillment — has come to me only when I give to people in need with no thought of what it might do for me."

What would we guess is ahead for Paula? I understand she is involved as an activist for a woman who is incarcerated. It would be interesting to know more about this. Those of us watching her search and conquer can only wait for the next chapter. I have no doubt at all that there is more to come. She has definitely assumed the title of "change agent" and pushed it far beyond the norm.

Others

Life is a journey of discovery — and change is the catalyst, the energy source, that propels us toward self-acceptance, unconditional love for others, appreciation of life, and a relationship with God.

Dennis Wholey writes:

> Personal growth is at the heart of living. However, since human beings by nature seek security, one of life's greatest continuing challenges seems to be finding the courage to change. We are frequently offered the opportunity to change. More often than we'd like, circumstances beyond our control force us to leave an existing state of affairs— our "status quo"—and muddle through an uncomfortable time before arriving in a new situation. Even if we initiate the change ourselves, the transition process is difficult. In brief, change is the spiritual movement from holding on to letting go to getting there and starting all over again.[4]

"To myself, I seem to have been only like a boy playing on the seashore, diverting myself now and then finding a smoother pebble or a prettier shell than the ordinary, whilst the great ocean of truth lay all undiscovered before me."

—Sir Isaac Newton

Paula's Books:

Gott, Paula, *Jesus, Master of Science, Lessons of Light* (ISBN 1-59109-284-1)
 To order: Gott, PaxAmoLux, P.O. Box 21, Highlandville, MO 65669

Gott, Paula, *Enchanted Circle* (ISBN 1-59457-185-6)

Gott, Paula, *Gabriel's: The Message and Mysteries in Luke and Acts* (ISBN 1-59457-205-4)

Gott, Paula, *The Life and Adventures of Little Water Molly Cule* (ISBN 1-59109-284-1)
 To order: Booksurge, LLC. Web Site: www.booksurge.com

Profile 6: Sharon Kahmann

SHARON FOUND HERSELF in that time period of her life in which she knew there was more for her to do. Her children were growing up, and the jobs she had held all seemed insignificant, almost as though someone else held them. Her feelings were juxtaposed as she searched out the desires to be a fulfilling wife, mother and employee, knowing deep inside that there was something more waiting for her.

I remember the first time I saw her in the workplace. She came into the corporate workplace unprepared for what was ahead, appearing very shy and uncomfortable to me, but managing to sort through the mail. A friend had told me she was coming on board the railroad family and to make her feel welcome. She was assigned to the mail desk as most clerks were on their first day. It is supposed to be such an easy job, but, of course, it is not easy. The new person has no idea who any of these people are, nor where their offices are located. Even the mail position is intimidating at first. I introduced myself and asked her to have lunch with my group of friends. Then as my morning became very busy in my established routine, I forgot all about her. I went to lunch without her, and when I happened to remember, I frantically went back to find her. She was just standing there, a beautiful, sad picture. We made this into a funny story to share, but this incident may have been an omen for her in this particular work environment. She was not destined to become a railroad die-hard. There were a number of significant changes ahead for her.

She left when the downsizing began. She tried a number of jobs, most significantly working in her husband's architectural firm. She knew the business world she had come to know left her empty. The idea of teaching kept returning, but it would require a long and very focused school pursuit. It would take time and money. Her family was accustomed to her being available for their needs, and would they be supportive when her time was devoted elsewhere? Many questions. But, a plan was starting to emerge in her mind, and she was not able to hold back. She started investigating the educational options and made a decision. Southwest Missouri State University was going to have a new art student.

The love of art was in her family, and her husband's being an architect had also exposed her to a very important component of the artistic industry. Her love of beauty and creativity would serve her well as she approached her new pursuit.

This was a major change from homemaker, office worker, a variety of jobs here and there, to a professional. She was now entering the world of education via art. Challenges too huge to contemplate were looming. She had to step back and take one step at a time.

The first step was SMSU for her bachelor's degree. The second step was securing a masters degree from Drury University. The next step was landing a position in the Springfield School System. Now she had become a part of the continuous challenge of lack of enough money in the system for the arts, as well as understanding and meeting the educational system's demands and changes. As a teacher, she had to be adept at administering to governmental and leaders' edicts even when she might find personal disagreement. The teacher requirements are very much like any big business or government bureaucracy.

She understood the challenges, but was prepared to meet them and teach these little youngsters what art could mean to them. Art is sometimes ignored as an avenue to history, geography, psychology and business. Sharon made it one of her goals to focus her teaching toward assisting these little people to understand mankind through the many art mediums. The process began for her, and she was suddenly at peace with her decision. All the hours of study, commitment, being away from home and family, and hard work were worth the outcome. She felt at home in the classroom and loved to share what she had learned and knew through art.

Does she fit my definition of change agent? How could she not? The homebody went to school. It makes little difference when we make some of our changes, only that we do it when we know that we should. The time was right for her after her children were older and she had tried several other jobs. She had the added plus of experience as well as education to add to her teaching agenda. She definitely fits the criteria of change agent.

Outside

Education. There is a need in both the public and private sector for teachers, teacher's aides, counselors, technicians and administrative aides. There is a shortage of skilled technical workers and engineers, professionals needed to create, plan and develop tomorrow's new products. Approximately half of the Ph.D.s teaching in colleges and universities are foreign born. And Ph.D. minorities, desperately needed on U.S. engineering college campuses, comprise 1.7 percent of those holding this degree; over all, only 5.6 percent of Ph.D.s teach at the college level. Many college professors will be retiring during the 1990s. Result: Approximately 500,000 college teaching vacancies will occur in this decade.[5]

Lori Holyfield's exceptional insight in her book, *Moving Up and Out,* finds through her research connecting education and income some interesting facts such as:

- Sociologists tend to see education as a more important factor because the correlation is so simple — in general, the more education you have, the higher your income.
- Overall, those with a four-year college degree can expect to earn $1,420,850 in a lifetime, compared to someone with a high school diploma at $820,870. For high school dropouts, expected lifetime earnings drop to $608,810.
- While the link between education and income has always existed, some researchers argue that the relationship is more important than ever before as credentials become the badge of legitimacy.[6]

Profile 7: Belinda Neal

BELINDA WAS A junior in high school and had secured her place. She was popular, and it had never crossed her mind to think of living anywhere other than in Little Rock. She worked in the principal's office rather than participate in her physical education class so that she could be where the decisions were being made and involved in what was happening at the moment. She had completed the necessary credits for graduation early, allowing her time to work in an accounting office on a DECA (work) program. It was soon apparent that accounting functions were not her choice of work — no people, just numbers — but she was learning how business offices operated. She was much more satisfied c tivities where she could lead and plan. She could come up with all kinds of ideas, put the plan into action, and subsequently hand the work over to someone else. Her place in life was going just fine. Then the "bombshell" was dropped on her.

Her father worked for the telephone company and was being transferred from Little Rock to West Memphis, Tennessee. He might just as well have said they were moving to a foreign country. She could not leave at this time of her life. She wanted desperately to finish school here. Her uncle recognized that Belinda was college material and offered to let her stay with his family to finish high school and go to college in Little Rock. His own daughter was a brilliant student, and the two of them could adjust just fine to this type of arrangement. This offer was a blatant insult to Belinda's dad, as he felt strongly that he could and should be the one to take care of his own family. The offer and refusal would cause a rift in their family for some time.

They moved. The transfer threw Belinda 180 degrees from the world that she knew. She considered it hell. She was the new girl. It was apparent to her that the girls hated her. She had nightmares and could not sleep. Many of the students were into drugs, and it seemed the druggies were the only people who befriended her. She went to school in her neat, preppy cloths and they were all in ratty, baggy jeans. Apparently the dress code was quite different from the way students dressed at home. She couldn't stand to be in this situation. Her boyfriend back home told her to come home, "We are getting married." She went to high school her senior year married. The marriage lasted three years and there were no children. She jumped from one dilemma into another one, but she simply could not make the change from her school at that time. In the future she would make many changes, but change agent she had not yet become. At this point in her life, she could only survive.

Job hunting in Little Rock would start the career moves. She found herself driving the wrong way on a one-way street to answer an ad. It was a creepy dental office with a creepy dentist. She ran out of the office and down the street, out of breath, leaning on the building. Was he really the lecher she thought he was, or was something else going on within her? She composed herself, checked out the next job opening, accepted the position and went to work as a typist for $400 a week at an insurance company. She was able to move up in position and pay within a short time with another insurance company. This company was in a big, beautiful bank building with gorgeous guys. She was single and starting to grow up in a number of ways. She was not a change agent yet. At this time in her life, she was a good-looking young woman trying to enjoy life after some setbacks. Her youthful marriage of convenience was over and she was on her own. She had stayed with each insurance job about a year and had now moved to her third insurance company. The agency was on the ground floor with a glass front. Three thousand people passed through every day. It was definitely a see and be seen location.

She met the man who would be her children's dad while working for this company. He was a stockbroker, nine years her senior. He had a nice car, was mature, and took her to nice places. She was probably drawn to the security and what he could provide. They were married and moved to Russellville, Arkansas. She was 22 years old, and most of her decisions were made on a whim. Where was the planner and organizer of the past? It seemed that after the trauma of the West Memphis move that her entire personality had changed. Planning was out; change was in. But was it the kind of changes that were productive for her. It did not occur to her that they would be *staying* in Russellville forever; she thought it was temporary. Another disappointment. The town appeared to her to be a small, cliquish town. She did not feel welcome. There was a definite lack of excitement. She felt the women were twenty years behind the women in Little Rock. What had she done? Was this another big mistake?

In her mind she knew it was time to get a job. She went to the insurance agency in town for an interview. The questions came, "What does your father do?" "Where do you go to church?" She knew the questions were illegal, but it was too mind-boggling to know what to say. Knowing better, she took the job. He came out of the office on the first day, "Get me so and so on the line." He was very precise, pausing to ask, "Are you with me?" When she would be near the absolute brink, there would be his look of "That's enough, young lady." She died (in a sense) that day. This man seemed to be from another century.

The next career change would be the newspaper office for seven years as a sales representative. A big disappointment would happen that would be instrumental in her decision to finally get that degree that was waiting for her. A marketing director position would open up that looked like it was made for her. The job description fit her. The position was working with the hospital ads. She just knew she could make them look so good. In the meantime, her best friend graduated from college and was working in the accounting department at the hospital. Belinda submitted her resume and talked with her friend about the job. Nothing happened. Belinda came in contact with the acting director and was told she did not get the job. She was falling through space, ears ringing, her heart stopped, the position was filled. They gave the job to her best friend. She did not even know her friend had applied for it. Her body was not there anymore. She could not function, could not breathe. She managed to get into her car and drive home. She went to her neighbor's for support. The neighbor did not understand. She went on and on about what kids want. The neighbor's husband was not supportive; he didn't even have a job. Another neighbor poured her a glass of wine to try to calm her. From her neighbor's home she saw her friend drive into her driveway. She could not talk to her at this time. Belinda's husband still did not know what was going on. The understanding was slowly coming to her. Her friend had the degree; she did not. She was probably never seriously considered for the job. Her friend phoned and Belinda simply told her she was busy; she found she could not be mean to her. She felt betrayed, but as time went on she would come to understand that her friend just didn't have the heart to be honest with her. She knew she had to do some planning. The end justifies the means kept repeating itself in her mind. What it meant exactly for this moment she wasn't sure.

To quote Belinda, "The marriage went south." This story about Belinda deals with her growth and acceptance of the changes that came her way. Her changes were like most of us; they came about through what seemed to be necessity. Her personal life was at a very low point at this time, and the physical abuse was becoming too much to deal with. Coping with abuse is such an assault to the mind that most people feel as though they deserve such treatment. Her physician through both children and most of the ten years she had been in this town let her know he would always be there for her if she ever needed him. A very personal incident happened in which Belinda had to allow both her old friend and her physician to help her. She had to get out of the marriage to survive. There was no money and no family. The doctor helped her. He assisted with money and any other help she needed in order to move. Very soon she was in an apartment. And before she had time to really heal from the last encounter, she found herself married to the doctor.

It was her third marriage, and she had entered an entirely new lifestyle. They combined their lives, merging her two children and his three. She was a stay-at-home wife for one year. He insisted she get an education. The marriage did not work out. Belinda had to start over again. And every time it was harder. His children phoned from time to time, telling her to come back home, but they were not right for each other and they both knew it. He wanted to "save" her, and she was too independent for that. His idea for her was to capture her in the big house. He wanted her to have nothing to do with her family because he wanted total control. He traumatized her children. He became impassioned when her son would not eat his squash. Her son left the home.

Belinda moved into an apartment again, the cheapest one she could find. Before she got on her feet again, she would stoop to food stamps and housing assistance. Another failure?

There were no longer any options. Belinda stepped back and assessed what had been going on. She was always moving ahead in her jobs and learning, but her personal life was filled with turmoil. She went back to what she had always done best even as a very young girl, planning. She stayed in Russellville, and in 1994 she graduated from Arkansas Tech University. Belinda turned her life around. She has been married for eight years now to a wonderful man. He had never been married and had no children. They dated for a year and did not rush into marriage. Belinda worked for the Russellville School District before going to her position at Lawson Mardon Thermaplate.

She started as a temporary assistant, moving to office administrator, then to human resources manager. She studied continuously in order to pass the requirements to complete her Professional of Human Resources Certification. This certificate requires preparation and determination to complete. Many people take classes in management development at the college level in order to pass the test. This was both a personal and professional achievement.

There were opportunities to secure promotions, but somehow her personal life always messed things up for her. There was always an adjustment that created moves or separations. The most important thing to remember about Belinda is her perseverance. She just kept getting back up after the falls. Disappointments and fear followed her, but she did not give in. She is more than a change agent; she is a survivor.

More

After a while you learn
The subtle difference between
holding a hand
and chaining a soul
and you learn
that love doesn't mean
leaning
and company doesn't always mean
security.
And you begin to learn
That kisses aren't contracts and
presents aren't promises
and you begin to accept your defeats
with your head up and your eyes ahead
with the grace of a woman
not the grief of a child.
And you learn
To build all your roads on today
because tomorrow's ground is
too uncertain for plans
and futures have a way of falling down
in mid-flight.
After a while you learn
That even sunshine burns
if you get too much
So you plant your own garden
and decorate your own soul
instead of waiting for someone to bring you
flowers.
And you learn
that you really can endure
that you really are strong
and you really do have worth

And you learn
and you learn
with every goodbye
you learn…
— *From "After A While," by Veronica A. Shoffstall* [7]

Profile 8: Alice Williams

HOW WOULD I know to tell you about Alice Williams, a survivor of extreme circumstances any time in history, but especially difficult in the late '30s, if her story had not been so special that it had to live on through time? Her grandson Rich shared her story with me, and I had the opportunity to visit with her daughter to get more details of how Alice accepted the situation given her and proceeded to make the changes necessary to go on. Rich remembers with fondness how she fixed him soft-boiled eggs with butter and crumbled crackers for a special treat. This is only a small example of the nurturing spirit dwelling within Alice. Her granddaughter relates how she still gains strength from her example. She was a pretty woman with lovely dark eyes and hair, energetic, looking forward to making a home for her family and doing what women of that era did with their time.

Finding herself as a young woman in the depression era with three children and another on the way was creating unexpected difficulties for everyone. The customary expectations of being a homemaker and taking care of her husband and children were made difficult due to the lack of jobs available. Her daughter Mary also had a child on the way. Mary's three siblings were Margaret, Jane and Donald. Alice was very mindful of the care required for her children and her grandchild. Jobs were very hard to find, and her husband, Oscar Richard Williams, whose friends called him Dick, was faced with a huge responsibility. Just when you think you have your plate full and cannot accept anything else, tragedy can strike. And an enormous tragedy did strike this young family. Dick was injured in an auto accident when he was around forty years old and was not expected to live. The accident happened in Moberly, Missouri, and since he was not expected to recover, his multiple broken bones were not set.

But Dick surprised everyone and did live. Now the surgical process to break the bones and set them properly would take many months. Alice must take care of Dick through the long months of rehabilitation, but what about the children? Daycare centers available today did not exist then. There was no money for that kind of care anyway. The decisions were hanging over her in such magnitude, that like all of us when under great stress, she probably functioned only by habit. Eventually Jane was sent to live with an aunt for two years, and her older sister was sent to live with another aunt. Other members of the family, especially Dick's sisters and Alice's mother, helped Alice with her children. We must understand the family circumstances to understand some of the drastic changes taking place and the changes ahead for Alice.

Dick's brother-in-law was a physician and had kept a close eye on this family who were in such dire circumstances. His medical knowledge was utilized at this time and would be an influence on future decisions for Alice. He had seen her rise to whatever occasion came to her more than once. One time she asked him for smallpox vaccine to inoculate some children. At first he thought she meant one person, or maybe her children. But no, she meant the entire school. Small school though it was, this was quite an undertaking. He managed to secure the vaccine, and she proceeded to inoculate each child.

It was quite evident that she evaluated her options and found she had few, but decided to be a risk taker well ahead of her time. She assessed the facts, several children she was responsible for, a husband who was recovering but would never be able to work at the potential he once did, no home of their own, and all the savings were gone. She could have just given up and hoped that family and neighbors would take care of them. But Alice had a better plan. She decided to take the training and become an LPN. The era was the early '40s, and Alice was going to school to become a nurse at the age of 60. She had learned a lot about health care as she made the decisions in regard to the care of Dick, but she had no formal training in the field at all.

She enrolled in school in Kansas City for the training. The school would take approximately two years. She completed the time required for her certificate and went to work. She worked in this capacity until she was eighty years old. I can only imagine the anguish she must have felt as she turned over the care of her children to relatives, how she worried about keeping up with the younger students in the quest for good grades, how she must have yearned at times to be a homemaker in the traditional sense. But she persevered. Her children grew up, her husband lived 20 additional years after his accident, and Alice bought them a home in Kansas City and paid for it.

Alice probably never thought of herself as a change agent. She became one when it was necessary for what she considered the survival of her family. There was no time for dwelling on the "why," only time to make decisions on what to do next. Students today have the formal steps in decision-making, identifying the problem, evaluating the alternatives, making the choice, implementing and evaluating again. It is evident from the strong stance she took that Alice, by instinct, practiced excellent skills in decision-making.

Her legacy to her family is magnificent. Even though not one member of her family would ever wish for her life to have taken the turn it did, they are so very proud of her. Even when her warm arms were not there to hold her little children, she made sure there were substitutes who cared about this family. She was a role model for all of us facing change and uncertainty.

Outside

In 1940 the labor force included 17.9% women ages 55 to 59. There were 33,226 experienced women workers and 1,072 new workers. The workforce included 14.4% women ages 60 to 64. This number included 20,430 experienced and 443 new workers.[8]

During this same time period there were 371,066 nurses, 362,897 being female all ages inclusive.[9]

Profile 9: Earl T. Frazier

What does a young man graduating from a small rural school do with his life after graduation? This young man had been diagnosed with weak eyes; therefore, he was not accepted into the military. This was at a time when World War II was taking many men into the unknown world of being a soldier for their country. Since this duty was no longer to be considered, what was he to do? The family farm was not big enough to support another family, so it was necessary to look beyond home. A job, where would he look? Buy a farm, where was the money? Get married, who and how would he support a family? It was 1934 and the same questions were looming over him in much the same way they are today in 2004. There appear to be many more options and opportunities today, but the big decision of what to do with the future is in every young person who faces the challenge of "choosing" the future.

The wanderer spirit took over. Earl, his sister and her husband took off for northern California to the orchards. They had heard there was money to be made, and Americans were in the midst of a severe economic depression. In addition, they would get a chance to see a big part of the United States they had never seen. This journey would take them halfway across the states from Missouri to the west coast. Keep in mind this was in the 1930s and the Ford they were traveling in was quite different from the automobiles of today. Modern conveniences such as an air conditioner were not even thought about for the average consumer. The ride was beginning.

When they arrived at the designated orchard, they were given a job and paid up to seventy-five cents an hour. That amount does not seem like much money, but back home there were no jobs at all.

Within six months they decided it was time to go back to Missouri. His sister and her husband decided to stay in Missouri and farm. Earl would make another trip to the west coast with a friend, but he would soon decide that he also belonged back in Missouri and would begin what would be his lifetime home. Earl had saved some money and hoped to buy a small farm, raise some cattle and milk cows to make a living. He had realized that this was in his blood and where he was most content. There was something about the land and the amazing way it had come through his great-grandfather down through the generations. He felt a connection with the earth and nature and would spend his life trying to stay on that farm.

It was also time to consider looking for a real girlfriend, one who might become important enough to marry. His friend, Byron Ghan, introduced him via a blind date to Glenna, and this girl became his wife during the early 1940s. They rented a farm, and when they could afford the down payment they bought one. Along came two children and more obligations. Money needs were mounting up, and at times Earl became almost consumed with worry. At this period in the small rural area where he lived, farmers worked together. During harvest or hay season, sharing work was a way of life. Wives cooked big lunches for the workers and life became routine.

During the fifties change was imminent for this young family and many others. There were major droughts and simply just not enough money to make it on the farm. What to do? Several neighbors had already made the decision to seek employment in Springfield, the largest town near to the rural area, but which was still 25 miles away. Earl's wife was especially helpful, as she would go to work at the garment factory periodically to help in the family situation. At this time in history, this was unusual for women to work outside the home. She was the only wife of the neighbors who chose to help in this way, which probably caused considerable questions from others. But even with the help, it was evident; he would have to go ahead with a major change.

Earl was the "fill-in" rural mail carrier for a time, and the young family had hoped this would be enough extra income to keep things the way they were. It was not enough.

Several of the neighbors were already working at the Industrial Products Plant, and being connected to someone always eases the way somewhat. This plant would become Kraft Foods, and Earl would work there 27 years. He retired while companies were still encouraging older workers to stay as long as they could. He left because he wanted to give his job to one of the newer workers who needed it more than he did. He had not forgotten how overwhelming it was at that stage of life. But another change would be coming. He just ran a few beef cattle on the farm, and that required very little time. His main hobby was horseback riding, and that, too, took little time for him. He kept a few horses, went on trail rides, and that hobby would be a lifelong enjoyment. But he still had time on his hands. Glenna, his wife, had found her niche in life as she, too, had several career changes and hobbies. He knew he must find another career/job.

The new job would be to drive a school bus for the Clever School District. Another challenge. His family did not think he would have the patience to handle a bus load of loud, energetic children. But they were wrong. He met the challenge well and would do this job for five years.

What does this example of change say to those who are embarking on their career walk? Earl is an example of making career moves when it is necessary. He found his wanderer spirit could be satisfied with an occasional vacation. His fulfillment would be reached while working the land and being involved with animals. When this was not possible, then he would join the industrial revolution and work in a factory environment. When this period would close, then he would assess what was available and move forward into the next phase of career change.

Earl was one of five children, and the entire family lived to an elderly age, staying within a five-mile radius of the original childhood home. They were hard workers and made career choices similar to Earl. One exception would be a sister who broke the gender boundaries of that day and became a postmaster. She broke many rules in this capacity. She traveled extensively to postmaster conventions and meetings. She also accepted state offices in the organization and excelled in that field. Her political views became quite different from her family, causing some strife within the group. But she, too, still stayed in the area near her birthplace.

Earl has been given a life of subtle as well as dramatic changes in which he handled making what he considered to be the best choices for what was available. Everyone at some point in their lives will face choices, and those choices will produce change. When we look at other people and how they handled these choices, maybe it will make it easier for the rest of us. Earl moved from agricultural to industrial to service in his career moves. Young people today quite possibly will move from service to technology and back to service. And as Earl did, most of the time there will be combinations of two or more types of work going on at the same time.

If you dare to be a risk-taker, then hold on for the ride!

Outside

World War I and Prohibition occurred during a time of rapid technological change, egocentric celebrities, widening class divisions, crumbling trusts and unions, and expert—but weak—political leadership. Following World War I, the public immersed itself in moral crusades (League of Nations, Prohibition, women's suffrage). By the 1920s, a fun-filled financial boom was framed by pessimistic debates over drugs, sex, money, cynicism, violence, immigration and the family.

The Great Depression and World War II began suddenly with the Black Tuesday stock market crash. After a three-year economic free fall, the Great Depression triggered the New Deal revolution, a vast expansion of government, and hopes for a renewal of national community. After Pearl Harbor, America planned, mobilized and produced for war on a scale that made possible the massive D-Day invasion (in 1944). Two years later, the crisis mood eased with America's surprisingly trouble-free demobilization.

The G.I. Generation developed a special and good-kid reputation as the beneficiaries of new playgrounds, scouting clubs, vitamins and child-labor restrictions. They came of age with the sharpest rise in schooling ever recorded. As young adults, their uniformed corps patiently endured depression and heroically conquered foreign enemies. In a midlife subsidized by the G.I. Bill, they built gleaming suburbs, invented miracle vaccines, plugged missile gaps and launched moon rockets. Their unprecedented grip on the presidency began with a New Frontier, a Great Society, and Model Cities, but wore down through Vietnam, Watergate, deficits, and problems with "the vision thing." As senior citizens, they safeguarded their own "entitlements" but had little influence over culture and values. [10]

During 1940 there were 552,480 men employed in Missouri, 89,600 were not employed.[11]

There were 2,899,780 out of 7,988,343 total employed in the agricultural division. [12]

Another interesting statistic for this family was the postmasters in the workforce during 1940. There were a total of 239,813, with 204,857 being male and 34,956 being female.[13]

[1] Vago, Steven, *Social Change, Second Edition* (Prentice-Hall, NJ, 1989), p.177.

[2] Bobbitt, Sharon A., *Characteristics of Stayers, Movers, and Leavers: Results from the Teacher Followup Survey, 1994-95, Highlights & Introduction* (U.S. Department of Education, Washington, DC, 1991, first printing), Internet: http://nces.ed.gov/pubs97/97450-0html.

[3] The Saudi Arabian Information Resource – OPEC Formation (Internet 10/31/02), pp.1-2.

[4] Wholey, Dennis, *The Miracle of Change* (Pocket Books, New York, 1997), p. 3.

[5] Connor, J. Robert, *Cracking the Over-50 Job Market* (Plume, New York, 1992), p.21.

[6] Holyfield, Lori, *Moving Up and Out* (Temple University Press, Philadelphia, 2002), p.57.

[7] Wholey, Dennis, pp. 228-229.

[8] Source: Department of Commerce, Bureau of the Census, Sixteenth Census Reports, Population, Volume III, p. 123.

[9] Ibid, p. 133.

[10] Strauss, William and Howe, Neil, *The Fourth Turning* (Broadway Books, New York, 1997), pp. 135-136.

[11] Source: Department of Commerce, Bureau of the Census, Special Report of 16th Census, Families, General Characteristics, p. 131.

[12] Source: Department of Commerce, Bureau of the Census, 16th Census Reports, Population, Volume III, p. 132.

[13] Ibid, p. 134.

AFTERWORD

WE BURIED JIM today. My book is concentrated on professional change, not my personal life. So, why am I telling you about Jim? I wanted to share my professional story with you, to assist you when you were faced with work-related decisions. The family plays a significant role in those decisions and changes. For this particular book, I felt it necessary to share my feelings in regard to career changes from my own viewpoint. It is designed as a book to accompany the textbook as an additional read suggested by the professor.

So, again, why on earth am I telling you about Jim?

I am sharing this personal story because I watched a beautiful display of acceptance. Acceptance of diversity in others. I believe I witnessed a great example of change.

Jim was 60 years old, but had lived enough life experiences to be twice that age. He had an engaging smile, a generous nature, and was easy to love. He is my cousin, and we grew up together. This is the beautiful story.

The memorial was non-traditional. We were supposed to be there at 11 a.m., but there was no "real" preacher to say the comforting words. His son tried to talk, but it was too emotional; his niece who sings professionally did sing, but it was almost impossible due to the circumstances. Very soon my mother got up from her seat and started walking forward. My husband on one side of me, and my daughter on the other side, were both looking at me and asking, "What is she doing?" I did not have any idea what she was doing either. This was so unlike her to do something that would draw attention to her as an individual. But there she was, standing at the podium. She recited a beautiful poem and shared her love for her nephew. She simply said, "Goodbye to my nephew, my friend, my neighbor … I loved you and I will miss you." We were all crying. Soon, another aunt was walking to the podium, telling a cute little story. Now, we were all smiling. Another cousin said a prayer. There were no dry eyes. Still, this story is not unlike stories many of us could tell who have had to give up loved ones. And why do I think it has anything to do with change?

Most of my family grew up in a very traditional church and very conservative background. Jim, on the other hand, had been reared in California and had lived a sometimes-controversial lifestyle. Jim's mom and dad had been divorced when their two children were small, and the children always spent summer school vacations in Missouri with us. They were the "city" cousins, and we felt they knew a lot more about important issues than we did. Jim informed us at a very young age as to what the word "pregnant" meant and other important pieces of information that I am sure we really needed. These cousins, along with our Wichita, Tulsa, and any other place they happened to live, all became like siblings when they arrived for their time at our grandparents' farm in the country.

The grownups had grownup problems, and we were kept in the dark about a lot of things. On several occasions even after I was grown, I would phone my parents at their home, ask where Mother was, and Dad would tell me that she was on her way to California to be with her sister. Her siblings were with my California aunt when she married, when she was divorced, and when she was sick. They were with her when she died. They were now with her son as he was being buried in their family plot.

The funeral home was full for Jim's memorial. The well-dressed conservative family. And the friends. The friends came together in a roar. They were on their Harleys, lots of bandanas, lots of black leather. At one time we would have been told that they were Hell's Angels by our parents and to have nothing to do with them. Today it is different. We have all changed.

We had the service. We traveled the 10-mile trek to the cemetery. Three or four family cars with the ashes, then the bikers, and then the rest of us. Oncoming cars respectfully stopped for us to pass. The aunts passed out the songbooks at the cemetery. To everyone! We sang two hymns around the burial plot. The dirt was pushed in, flowers placed lovingly on the grave. He was placed next to his mother and our grandparents. Among the family, the bikers, and the neighbors, the acceptance of all was evident. We were all there for one reason. It made no difference what we wore or what mode of transportation we used. Out of love — we buried Jim today.

Coping

Our family has been touched with alcohol addiction, death and divorce, sickness, job loss. But, if you were to visit us on a holiday, birthday or family visiting from out of town, you would see a group singing around the piano, playing games at the table and eating the most delicious food in the world. All our coping skills have been needed from time to time. A loving, supporting family is a gift many people do not have. If you have that gift, then you are fortunate, as my family is. They will be worth a future book!

ABOUT THE AUTHOR

Photo: Abrahamson

CURRENTLY LIVING IN Springfield, Missouri, Judy Frazier Compton has chosen to write this book to help anyone who is addressing life changes. Many big changes have come her way. Sometimes there was trepidation and a little guilt; other times excitement and challenge. But always, that old enemy — fear — wanted to ruin it for her. Dr. Compton had been told from childhood that women belonged in the home, and her personal desire to develop a career often brought inner conflict. She spent the major part of her life working for a large railroad and managed to continue with her education as well. She holds a bachelor's degree in business administration, a master's degree in liberal arts and a Ph.D. in international business law. She now works as a teacher, writer and motivational speaker. Dr. Compton believes that, while nothing ever stays the same, we can all learn healthy coping skills to deal with unanticipated and unwelcome change, and hopes the stories she shares in *Back On Track* will inspire readers to accept the challenge of change. She invites you to come along for the ride.

For additional information or to schedule speaking engagements, please contact Dr. Compton at:

www.judycomptonbooks.com